To Yvone

From Louise

"God blessing always"

Poetry and Stories
Straight from the Heart

Poetry and Stories
Straight from the Heart

Dalsie Mullings Powell

Published in 2005 by Stamford House Publishing

A CIP catalogue record for this title is
available from the British Library

ISBN 1-904985-30-0

Stamford House Publishing

INTRODUCTION

I was born in the island of Jamaica, West Indies, in the Parish of St Elizabeth, in the District of Dalton. I am the sixth child of Leslie and Iris Mullings. I went to a primary school which was owned by the Anglican Church of England. I did not get any academic qualification, because of caring for my siblings and other problems that goes with it. I am from a family of twelve children. I came to England in 1961. I worked at a factory for four years under very hard conditions. The word to describe it was a place of hard labour. I had four children therefore my working days at the factory were limited. I started to work at home, as a milliner so that I could take care of my children. I started to write poetry in 1987 after returning from a holiday in Jamaica. There were issues I did not like there, hence when I returned I started to write poetry. It was to my horror when I returned to hear of the Hungerford massacre, and within a month later there was the hurricane, the most devastating one this country has observed.

I had two awards for my outstanding achievement in poetry. Another two I was told I would have but I did not attend the convention because I was ill. I was sent a medal from the National and International Library of Poetry. I was even invited to go to Washington DC to read poetry on their Poetry Day. I am published in sixty magazines, and thirty eight anthologies, and also I had a small booklet published. I hope I will give joy and peace and happiness to each and everyone who reads my poems and stories. May the Blessing of the Lord Jesus Christ be with you all.

Dalsie Mullings Powell

FOREWORD
LITERARY CONSULTANT'S REPORT

Ms Mullings Powell's work has much to recommend it and is a fine example of modern poetry. She writes in a very fluid and natural manner, unconstrained by current trends and rigid literary boundaries, thereby making her work all the more appealing to the average poetry reader. Having said this, the poet makes excellent use of a variety of poetic techniques where they suit her purpose but at all times ensures that the actual content of the poem is more important than its form.

I would advise that this poetry be published as a stand alone collection as including different types of writing in the work would detract from the verses. Ms Mullings Powell shows herself to be a competent and effective writer of both prose and drama but it is in poetry that her true talents lie. Additionally, there is a definite market for collections of verse of this kind whilst miscellaneous and varied works tend to prove much less successful.

In its current format, I do feel that the collection is too lengthy and would benefit from being edited down somewhat. This would result in a more manageable and reader-friendly collection. I would also leave the way open, should this first volume be successful, for further collections to be produced.

The poet tackles some very large themes in the work, highlighting her own opinions and ideas on them all. Justice, civilisation, nature, war, religion, feminism and love are all touched upon and Ms Mullings Powell discusses these, some of which are intense or contentious subjects with mastery and skill. Indeed, the collection is likely to be all the more impacting because of this and will in turn challenge, provoke and inspire the reader.

The character of the poet is expressed throughout the collection and it is very clear that she does not pick up her pen lightly, but instead writes with a great deal of care and forethought on the topics that affect her most deeply. The passion and sincerity of Ms Mullings Powell is one of the elements that makes her work so unique and should endear the reader towards her.

We live, as the poet subtly points out, in an ever changing world and are constantly faced with both trials and rewards in our daily lives. Ms Mullings Powell has great empathy with her reader, choosing to write on many of the subjects which concern her most at the present time. This capturing of the current mood makes the collection a poetic odyssey for our time and can be seen to express the emotions of an age.

Many if not all, of the poems in the collection are open to a wide variety of interpretations and will mean different things to each individual reader. This is where the true beauty of Ms Mullings Powell's poetry lies, in its universality, and it should be attractive to the widest possible audience as a result.

Similarly, some verses have a deeper, or hidden meaning which may not be immediately obvious to the reader. Ms Mullings Powell's works are extremely thought provoking and evocative because of this, leading the reader to pause and ruminate on the subject matter of her works for some time. When the hidden meanings are unlocked, they are likely to stay in the mind of the reader for quite some time, having a positive effect on his life.

Another very appealing feature and one which will ensure the lasting merit of the collection, is the somewhat religious nature of the work. Ms Mullings Powell is profoundly concerned with the state of our planet, the state of the world's psyche and the increasing lack of moral backbone we demonstrate in our lives. She strives towards, as may of us do, some kind of higher power and searches for the meaning and reason in our lives. However, her poetry does not lean overtly towards one particular religious denomination and is suitable for devotees of a variety of faiths. Indeed, rather then being seen as religious, her work should best be viewed as spiritual.

Though the technical side of the work takes second place to the poems' content, Ms Mullings Powell still shows herself to be an accomplished writer. She utilises both rhyme and blank verse, thereby creating a very plausive variety of form, and employs tools such as repetition, alliteration and assonance where appropriate.

It goes without saying that predicting exactly how successful a book will be is incredibly difficult, if not impossible. Various factors need to be taken into consideration, and even though a book may be first class in terms of content and composition, it may still struggle to enjoy the critical acclaim and long-lasting success it deserves. However, I do feel that this useful work merits publication and should be well received by the relevant reading audience.

CIVILISATION

When man looked at this world
And the goodness therein,
He wondered at first, why should there be sin,
He looked at the sky, he looked at the trees,
He looked at the land, he admired the seas,
He looked beyond the clouds and sighed
Whoever you are, whatever You are
'Thank You Lord.'
Then he discovered that this world is round
He had a bright urge for new lands to be found
He started to stray to faraway places,
'Sadly he started to wear two faces.'
He developed the taste for milk and honey,
The time had come for mankind to have money
And then came the need for more and more.
Now look at the difference between rich and poor,
Now look at the world's needs
Caused by our enormous greed,
Now look at the wars and look at the scars,
In order for one man to have ten shares
Nine must go without whilst always in tears.
May God give us grace to be led by Wisdom
For us to get a fair share of the Kingdom.

LEADERS AWAKE

Leaders of the nations awake, we need your view,
To others' plight, 'We are seeing a changing world'
As the years advance, 'See the world as it is.'
View the people, the animals, the trees that live in it.

There may be drought, volcano or earthquake
Take a grim look, then examine the causes and its effect.
Help those that are in need and distress,
For we are in a world of changing tide.

Cast cares aside, live on our guide?
We are seeing things we didn't visualise,
And we need your help and your light,
Leaders of the nations examine your flight
We are in danger, for the ozone is in sight
And violent death and sleaze combine.

FATHER I'M COMING HOME

I am coming home to you Father dear
With my heart full of joy and gladness;
Onward I will march with the Pilgrims
Where I'll join the angels with your Christian band.

I will view you on the horizon,
Wearing a robe, radiantly white
'Rejoice for I am coming with love and peace divine.'

Through forestry deep I'll pass,
With birds and animals that sound alike
'To seek your joy and peace and love'
Where sinners have not been to pollute the air
And ancient flowers perfume the breeze.

Rejoice I say rejoice,'
For I am coming home to you at last.

ARE WE TO BE BLAMED

Sometimes we are to be blamed for the corruption of our children.
We refuse to discipline them in the same manner of which we
were disciplined.
Children can be little angels one minute and devils the next.

They are not wise to know right from wrong,
They are not born with habits of obedience,
Nor of self-discipline and respect.
We must teach our children morals.

'Remember today's unrestrained child is tomorrow's problem
person,'
'As the street crimes and house breaking shows.
Parents and others in authority must set an example;
'Our children are failing and we have been warned.'
If society fails our children, then we'll have problems on hand.

Let awesome goodness rattle through the hearts of our little
children
Then earth will rattle with awesome 'gladness'
And may God give us grace to erase our mistakes,
That we may have our morals returned.

LIFE

There are some things so familiar between
Humans, birds, animals, insects and plants,
We all live and we all die
And all depend on each other for our being.

Life begins as a seed,
It continues to grow until it dies.
Life has roots and life has branches
The roots are our ancestors
While the branches are our children,
Whether it is human, birds, animals, insects and plants.

Life is full of mysteries,
And life is full of surprises.
Let the life we live be full of grace,
Let it be pure and safe and sound.
Live your life as clean as you can
And remember the others as you go along.

JUST LIKE CRAZY

I'll hum with humility as I hug, the hoola hoop
In the hospital there is so much hostility
That the patients are scared to use the hose.
The sound of hounds in the house
Is just like a hot-house.

You put pen and ink to my injury
And it will be an invitation to my interest.
There is so much horror in my horoscope
That I dread the hornet in my house.

By having a strike I will be stripped
Of the title of being the greatest string bean eater.
I am just like crazy, to sound like crazy, crazy it is, 'eh!'

DOOM AND GLOOM AT CHRISTMAS

There is no room for doom and gloom,
There is faith, love, hope and joy.
Get ready for we are here in style
To welcome the festive cheer;
Many went East, many went West,
Many up and down,
Trying to have a magical dream.
Come ye faithful, come ye loner,
Come and enjoy the turkey and the golden grain,
With wine from the vineyard in our yard.
The hope that soothe the hearts for years
Will embrace the love that shines beneath,
That's why there's no room for doom and gloom,
It's Merry Xmas everyone.
Cheer the hearts of broken thoughts and fear,
Let the festive season rattle on.
Give us the pleasure of sure reward,
Guide the footsteps that go away;
Wash the guilt of strains and stains away
For there's no room for doom and gloom.

I LOVE YOU MY DARLING

I love you my darling,
At night when I go to bed;
I think of you and I cry.

I want you to touch me
I want you to caress me,
Hold me, squeeze me, love me.

Breathe on me, breath of life,
Breathe on me, breathe on m e
As deep as you can.

Hold me, hold me, hold me,
Squeeze me, squeeze me, squeeze me,
Kiss me, Kiss me, kiss me.

Sing to me, smile with me
Dance, dance, dance with me.

MUSIC AND DANCE

We shall be dancing at the hall tonight
We shall be dressed in long ball gowns,
Under the chandelier we will rock
And we shall roll to the music of our band.

When the clock strikes one, we'll rock along
To the sound of music in our land
'Rock' to the music, 'rock,'
'Shake' to the music, 'shake.'

In the morning's dimming light,
We've the motivator, day and night;
Life would be an error, without our music
Which appeals to the humble and the noble.

You and I can be prophets of our dance,
When we dance to the music from our band.

WHEN I FALL IN LOVE

When I fall in love
I'll make sure the lad is a friend
And not just a lover.
I didn't know love was so hard
To find until I met you,
If I hold on we will realise
That our love will never die.
Words are demanding,
Hearts are entwining,
Our love is refreshing,
And so may the fun around us grow.
'You know darling,' I will always love you,
You are my lover, my companion and my friend.

I will love you when the sun is shining,
I'll love you when the rain is pouring;
With all my heart and soul
I'll continue to love you.
'Just tell me you will be there
When I need you,'
You are the sunshine of my life,
You are the lillies of the valley,
'You will forever be the diamond in my ring.'
Come and sit beside me, while I serenade you
With my love song.

HURRICANE GILBERT

Some years have passed so let it go,
Pleased to know that they are here.
When drought is here they forget
Hurricanes are still around
To kill the crops in the fields below.
They call me hurricane Gilbert
For I'm so ruthless a hurricane to fear.
I strangle the nation at their peril;
Droughts end, rain falls, wind blows
But me hurricane keeps smashing along.
There's no limit to the hazards I cause
For there's no one for me to fear.

I kill their humans, I kill their flocks,
I rip their roofs off their houses and schools
The houses so small I should call them sheds
For humans must suffer, for all I care,
They call me 'Gillie', a name to fear
For they're no match for me at all.
They cry for mercy, they run in fear,
'But I just keep smashing along'
Embrace yourself to meet the worst
For I'll be back in a few more years.

WE KNOW

We know what song to sing
In every peaceful home
We know what hymns declared
For every cathedral in the land
The music song and dance
In churches, halls and schools.

We know when hymns are sung
For everyone is glad
We know when lyrics are good
For every human will be singing.

We know when berries are ripe
For every bird is singing
We know when food is good
For everyone is eating.

God gave us wisdom to be used
And everyone should be wise

'Twas what we did that makes us great
So we'll go on to mightier stakes.

SO

So eloquent is your voice
So soft is your touch
So tender are your lips
So elegant are your steps
So beautiful is your body
So wonderful a person you are to me

Gasping in delight I gazed in your eyes
You are the motivator in my world
You are like the lillies in my valley
You are like the diamonds in my ring
And you are like the stars that shine at night
You and I could be prophets for our love

So beautiful are your eyes
So beautiful is your style
So wonderful a person you are to me
With great excitement I looked in your eyes
You are my lover a thousand times over
So our love will grow stronger and stronger.

I WALK THIS LEAFY LANE

I walk this leafy lane with trees along
To listen to a robin singing a song
The tune she sings is so melodious
I feel like dancing as I walk along.

High above the bushes I saw another
Which must have been her one true lover
His colours were so unusually bright
He thinks he is the king of the bushes.

He dances and displays his feathers
Like a leaf in the autumn wind
Amazingly she stops singing for a while
Just to watch her lover mesmerising her
With his beautiful feathers and wonderful motions.

She with her singing and he with his motion
Have kept me gasping with sheer delight
For a while I thought I was in a different world
When I saw this wonderful display of bird's emotion.

I think they could teach us a thing or two
How romantic I uttered!
'This is a manifestation of true love in motion'
If only we could show such love
Life would not be such a bore
'I'll continue to walk this leafy lane'
To hear little robin singing for her lover
While he mesmerises her with his motion.

WAR

War in the desert, war in the jungle,
War in the town, war in the house,
War of words, war of the bullet,
War that hit the nation at its peril

War with people, against people,
Animals against animals and birds against birds.

Why are we so cruel in this war torn world?
Why are we so sad, when we cultivate these wars?
This world would be a peaceful place
If only we did not have these dreadful wars.

War is like love, it always finds a way to rest in our hearts
War is like a disease of the brain,
That grips the world at its peril,
Wars are like words that blow unkind,
Which blows upon the armies of mine.

We sink to the depth of utter disgrace,
From which no one can ever shine.
War destroys new hope and grace,
War will take us to our graves.

War will make the victor stupid,
For which, the victim never forgets,
War lost, war won, war disgrace,
Alas! We will never forget our lot
And grieve for our loved ones as they rot.

LITTLE BIRDS SONG

With all the slush and snow along,
Earth is listening for little birds song.
We humans are here to celebrate
'For little birds are alive and singing songs.'

Away in the meadow they search for worms,
Up in the trees, they search for warmth,
Give them shelter to earth's gladness,
Let us have leaves for little birds goodness.

'Remember when winter is cold and frosty'
We were anxious to help little birds,
Not only with seeds, bread and worms
But with shelter in our loft and in our cages.

Give them spreading tree with plenty leaves
'Then they'll sing songs of awesome gladness.'
Remember the nightingale in the highest bush
'Singing songs of sweetest praises.'
If only you could know their words.
Only you could sing their songs
Then help the world to understand

Their song means so much to my ear,
To help me through my ensuing years.

THE PERIL IN OUR COUNTRY

I winced to see the peril in our Country today
The place in which things are happening
Before our very eyes.

Where there is no education
'Obviously' there will be no morals
Discipline has gone to the wind.

It is indeed a tragedy that our morals
Are gone, and peril is begun.
The consequences are becoming clearer
By every passing day.
We as individuals are not trained to see
Ourselves as responsible for our actions.

We are always thinking of one's self first
Self advancement, self indulgence
Is pure self greed, hence others are left
With what we think they should have.

Have we become over civilised?
Or are we just computerised.
May the goodness of light shine on us
For us to behold what we are doing
In this our wonderful country,
And may the peril go faster than it came.

THE RISEN SUNLIGHT/A VILLANELLE

The road is rough with a dark glow,
There lies the risen sunlight that hangs between,
The surface of the evening wind below.

Raindrops that came with riping fruitfulness,
Came flowers from the warming sun;
Concealing the love with harvest gratefulness.

Along the mountain with sharpened stones,
Lies the goat sheltering under the canopy below,
The surface of gathered bones.

Among the lillies the dawn awakens,
With misty dewdrop on the crop;
Which massages to the roots that we forsaken.

Farmers in bright summer frocks
Watch in awe at their embrace
To see the shepherds with their flocks.

The natives basked in lubricating sheen,
There lies the twilight of the evening rain,
With awesome fruits that lovers seen,
That catches the eyes of the village brain.

CONFUSED

Am I black or am I white?
Am I short or am I tall?
Am I rich or am I poor?

I know really who I am
I am the person from Angypong;
Who usually has my undies off
When they were on, they were on,
When they were off, they were off;
When the lights went out
I didn't have anything on!

Said one sharp eyed spectator,
'At least you got your tattoos on'
You really can sleaze, as you sneeze
No wonder you're chilly in the breeze!

COMING HOME

Coming home, coming home, I am coming home
Tell Mama and Papa, I am coming home
Tell brothers and sisters I am coming home
Grace and John will be there I'm told
So I am coming home.

Free at last, free at last, I am free at last!
Go shout it from the mountains
That I have gained freedom
And I am free at last to be home.

No more sorrow, no more tear
No more grief and no more pain
I am coming home, coming home
Prepare the fruits and the veg
For I am coming home, coming home

We will get together and forget our pain
For I am coming home, coming home
When the earth quake and the wind blew
We will be celebrating under the canopy of love
For this awesome love we have to share
May peace and love be the epitome of our dream
For all we need is love.

THE PAIN OF DRUGS

For all the power and wisdom we have
Earth is breaking into awesome madness
Let all within us feel the pain
Of human suffering in our plain.

'Perhaps' some will die of drugs so far?
If they have not prepared to have a spar;
Give us wisdom to earth's madness
Let us sing a song of awesome goodness.

'Get rid' of the suffering in our land?
Give us wisdom and caring thought
And let the wise come shining through
While earth is breaking into awesome gladness.

We, the nobility are to cheer
While the humble will stand and stare.

AND

And you and I and I and you
And they and them and us and we
And to eternity we shall run and play
And sweat and tears I cry for help
And sweet words to ban his boring ways
And round about my tears I sweat
And here on earth I view my plants
And sweet perfume that follows the air
And then between the leaves I saw a bee
And burning trunks with leafy twigs
And on the ground I play and dance
And on the flute I blew a tune
And to my maiden I sing with glee
And then on him I smile and wink
And here on my rug I stand
And listen to the sound of cockrells song
And then at twilight I found my lover
And with my lover I had a kiss
And you and me and them and they
Will be together in this our world
Tints, tones, shades and shapes
That's what are found on the meadow
On the woodland floor and on the valley.

WHEN I GET TO HEAVEN

When I get to Heaven
I will hear the angels sing
To everyone in Paradise.

High above the cloud I'll go
To mighty heights above the sky
To see my people so perfectly clean
Abraham will be there with a thrill
Waiting for me to show my skill.

I want to breathe the air so clean
Unpolluted by our sleaze
We are to be blamed for the hazard we caused
To mighty heights above the leaves.

When I get to Heaven, I will sing and dance
To the angels with my new skill
They would like to see my dance
So modern to match my song.

They were thrilled with glee
To see my every motion in Paradise
How divine the angels said
We are admiring your endeavours
To see me dancing in heavenly motions.

A VILLANELLE/MY SONG

I walk this store with dresses along
To see the dresses on their hanging rack
'Twas so exciting I burst into song.

Here I am humming my song
When seeing a shopper wearing a smock
'Twas so exciting we burst into song.

There you are singing my song
There they are having a snack
'Twas so exciting we started to jig along.

They are walking as they shop along
'Twas so exciting they started to mock
For we were singing a well written song.

Sing on! Sing on! A merry song
We are in this store to view your flock
Then barter as we select along.

Listen, listen, then dance along
Read my lyrics then buy my stock
Dance to my music for they're singing my song
Clap our hands as we sing along.

THE SKY AT NIGHT

I looked above the trees one night
Then wondered why the stars are so bright
In great amazement, I saw a shadow
Way above the clouds of moving wind.

I was so bewildered I called my friend
Just one look at that shadow I said
Gasping in the night and yet so frightened to say
It looks like our father from above.

Was He wondering where we've gone?
Or was He admiring the beautiful fruits our harvest brings
The Millennium is just a whisper away
So maybe He is admiring our dome
Or was He just fascinated by our gnomes?

Strange things happen in the sky at night
So wait for Him to ride the clouds
He loves His children who obey the rules
And He also loves an invitation to our hearts
Just keep a watch on the sky at night
For we'll never know when He's in sight.

WONDERFUL . . .

Sometimes we sit and wonder
How wonderful are the wonders of this world;
Wonderful World and beautiful people,
Have surrounded us with all the beauties of beauty.

How wonderful are the mighty oaks,
How wonderful are our great heroes;
How wonderful are our music and dance;
We are all so wonderful in this wonderful world.

The wonderful workers of all hearts
Have all the secret things in mind;
Of human thoughts and everything
To bind the wonders of this wonderful light.

Wonderful things we should acknowledge;
That the harvest has begun;
Where we gather up the crops
To feed the nations and our flocks.

This wonderful world with beautiful people
Has all the wonderful gifts to share;
So may we in our wonderful moments
Share our wonderful dreams.

OH MOTHER DEAR

'Oh Mother dear,' take my hand,
Take my hand less I fall
Falling from grace and falling in pain
I am your child in a changing world.

I have witnessed this my dear child
'It is here it is here my child.'
The world is changing fast, as we mingle in sin
'We pollute the air, as we fight for breath.'

Our morals, our freedom, our wealth
And our dignity is almost gone.
Oh help me in my plight 'Mother dear'
Help me as I cry in pain,
To redeem my rights as they slip away.

We have to get it right, so help me in my plight
I am your child, fighting in a fast changing world
'Oh Mother dear' take my hand
Take my hand, less I fall,
Oh take, take my hand Mother dear
Alas! My end is drawing near.

WAITING FOR A SMILE

Behold I'm sitting on the couch and watch,
Just looking at your face to see a smile;
But you don't smile anymore I sigh.

Waiting in pain to see you smile,
I wonder what I can do to see you laugh;
With that face I know so long ago,
My weary heart is full of your uncaring thought,
I'm slowly slipping away in a dreamy plight;
Waiting for you to smile and say you care.

My unwholesome thought to a melancholy you,
My weary heart is like a frightened cat;
'Just waiting in the shadows of darkened leaves.'
Swerving in solitude of a well built house
I'll seek salvation, in my darkened room.

SING IT

Sing, sing along, loudly down the road,
Let your voice be heard far and near;
Open your vocals loud and clear,
Let the drums echo as you sing and dance
Just keep singing as you go along.

How gracious are the songs you sang
How wonderful are the words and things
Keep on singing, as you go along
Sing songs of love and peace and joy,
Sing songs for dance as you jig along.

Sing it, sing it, sing it
Songs are the expression of great people
And so is it, for the poor and humble
Make merry by singing your songs.

NOSTALGIC

The past is in front of us
For we always remember it,
The present is here around us
'For it is happening now.'

The future is behind us
For we do not know what is happening next
'Nostalgic, nostalgic' we all should be nostalgic.

Prove to me what is going to happen tomorrow
For you are not sure of anything,
Prove to me what has happened yesterday
And you can write a book.

'Prove to me the future' for it may never be
Time present is the only time for thee.

I LOVE

I love the nuts in my fruit cake
With chocolate coated top;
The eating under the bridge below
The laughing down the road.

I love the green grass of Windsor
With big horses on the farm;
The Blacksmiths in their white aprons
The hammering in the shop.

I love the meadow of Windsor
With pheasants in the trees;
The nesting in the chestnut trees
With squirrels on the run.

I love the farm of Windsor
Underground up the road;
The lack of music everywhere
All human life is there, I say.

THE SHINING STAR

Have you seen the star
That bright shining star,
It is shining down on me
It is shining, it is shining
Let it shine, let it shine, let it shine,
On the moonlight night it is twice as bright
When it shines on my window
It makes my heart flutter
As it shines on my pillow;
So let it shine, let it shine, let it shine.

Let's sing about that star
That bright shining star;
It is shining down on me
It is shining, it is shining
Let it shine, let it shine.

Wine me, dine me, love me
While the star is shining
Let it shine through the mirror
Let it shine, let it shine, let it shine.
When the star shines bright
On the bright snowy night
I will be dreaming on my pillow
And waiting for you to dine me
So let it shine, let it shine, let it shine.

FROM ONE DIMENSION

When my end has finally come,
I would love to see with a different sight,
This planet getting smaller and smaller
While I'm ascending higher and higher
Above the cloudy sky I'll go,
How far how high I'll never know.
I will not die I'll pass away,
I'll go where there's no night nor day
And from dimension to dimension,
Only stopping when I reach that station.
I would like to write my memoirs here.
To read to those I love so dear,
And say farewell to my every friend.
My epitaph will say in the end,
Here lies my body and not my soul
Then my soul will go on to the spirit world.

SIN NO MORE

Sin no more my little sinner
Sin no more my little one;
Sin no more shall fail you
For Christ is here to guide you,
He will never forsake you,
Neither will He despise you.
How silently, how emotional,
His wondrous gift is given
He will repair your heart
In Heaven and no ear can hear His coming,
For he is silent as a lamb,
'So open your heart and accept our king'
'He is Christ and He will enter in.'
Up in the Throne on high!'
He will be riding in the sky!
With His angels by His side,
Some will carry the crown
Made of silver and realms of gold,
'So sin no more my little sinner'
Sin no more my little one.

EARTH'S JOY AND SORROWS

I looked beyond the clouds one night,
And wondered why the sky's so bright;
In great amazement I saw the moon and stars of light,
All beaming on earth's atmosphere
Low beyond the clouds or moving wind.

Upon waters pure and clear,
The golden moon is shining bright;
On rocks and trees and fire and foe,
I looked beyond the cloud and said
'How wonderful a world we have to explore'

Though joy and sorrow surrounds this earth,
May all our hearts be able to love,
This blessed earth wherein we live.

With arms to bound the endless wave,
And human with awesome minds;
Will look at this precious world,
With all its wonderful people
And beautiful things, then give a thought.

I looked beyond the clouds and said
'This is a wonderful, beautiful world!'

THE DESIRE WOMEN CRAVE FOR

Now that the victims triumph won
For they have got the desire they crave for,
Now we can clap our hands and shout for joy,
For women have won their victory.

Christ is so good and He is so true
He has changed the hearts of our men
For women, to deliver the Holy Sacrament.

They yearned for this for many a decade
But were denied the salvation they needed;
Years have changed and words have decayed
So have the thoughts of neglect and shame.

The Evangelistical hearing has given its best
For women to have desire they crave for
They are caring and they are so true
And they will have the love they command.

The spirit of love, the spirit of light,
The spirit of fire, the spirit of water,
Is all around us as we kneel and pray.
We must accept the spirit of change
For Christ is with us and will guide us
As we sing and pray

IT IS NOT LOVE

It is not love that taught me song
It is song that taught me love.
'Love is like the sweet apple Eve gave Adam'
With sweetness like that of honey
Love is bitter and yet so sweet
It is like a song we sing over and over
It is romance and not love
That taught me to sing
That's why I'm always singing love songs
The word I'm saying, I love you so much

In a heart of every thought we trust!
Which is full of love divine and faith
Good and pure and right for all
'That's why I'm always singing love songs.
Oh perfect love with hearts so strong,
Fill us with your awesome song,
Let the days and weeks go by
And send some more love to my clappy song.

THE POWER OF A BOXER

On a moonlit night, as we watch the fight
Both boxers are just as good
Let all within us see the power
And sweat pouring from their faces.

We know their power, their arrogance that proves
An evil scent of blood, pouring from their faces
We clap our hands, and shout for mercy
We are witnessing the power of our men.

Power to make one win, power to make one right
And power to give one the victory.
Power coming from the fists of men
Not from guns, bombs and sticks
From which no one can comprehend.

They score with numbers as they fight
The rounds from which they score the most,
One has won, the other has lost
One a happy face, the other a saddened mess.

In his heart and wounded pride
Let him forever, prove his worth
For he will be back with a mightier fight.

YOW YOW

Yow, love peace hair wax
That's what the Rasta man says,
He waves his hair and smokes his pot
And puts the man in blue in a spot.

Yow, the Rasta man walks and twirls
He knits his cap and plaits his hair,
He eats no pork, and he eats no ham,
Yow, yow, he says to his friends
Yow, he lives in Brixton, it is just like Kingston Town.

Yow, yow, this is Rasta man sister town
His lady is a queen and his daughter a princess
And they live, together as a perfect match,
Rasta man does not divorce,
Rasta man live in peace and harmony.

Yow, Rasta man loves the most and Rasta man boasts the most
Rasta man believes in peace and love to the human race.
Yow, Rasta man always say peace and love to his brother
And peace and love to his sister
Yow, that's how Rasta man says 'Hi.'

RESCUE

(This was dedicated to Terry and John when they were kidnapped, when on their missionary journey.)

Rescue me and I will return to comfort you
Try very hard for I am not safe
Rescue me when the rain stops falling
Rescue me when the wind stops blowing
Rescue me when others are sleeping
Rescue me when they are tired of asking
Rescue me when Mum and Dad have given up hope
Rescue me when the warrior is dealing.

When in distress to you I call
From you my rescue came
To clear my heart and sending peace
And everlasting joy to let me know how much you care

You rescued me and let those who did not try
Say what a lucky lad am I?
They will never understand how much you tried to rescue me.

I shall be paying with my diamond ring
I shall be paying with all my love
On my bended knees from which my rescue came
I shall never forget the things you did to rescue me.

I shall repeat this wonderful word
Rescue, Rescue, Rescue, you have rescued me.

THE MIGHTY MAN

Who was that Boy that Mary had?
It is The Mighty Man called Jesus!
Who is that Man the Wise Men visited?
It is the Mighty Man called Jesus!
Who is that Man the Wise Men brought
Gift of gold, frankincense and myrrh for?
It is the Mighty Man called Jesus!
Who is that Man, John the Baptist baptised
       In the River Jordan?
It is the Mighty Man called Jesus!
Who is that Man who helped Joseph in his
       Carpenter's trade?
It is the Mighty Man called Jesus!
Who is that Man who turned water into wine
At the wedding in Canaan?
It is the Mighty Man called Jesus!
Who is that Man who fed the multitude
From two small fish and five barley loaves?
It is the Mighty Man called Jesus!
I love that Man, that Man from Galilee
He is the Man we all called Jesus.
He is our Refuge and our Redeemer.
From Heaven above He came down to save us
From our pain and from our grief.
Yes, He is the Man! That Mighty Man called Jesus!

Biblical Quotation: 'Before Abraham was I am'

FREE OF THE CHAIN

Now I am free of the chain I have found salvation
Now I can proclaim from the mountain top
That I have gained my freedom at last.

'Twas in my twilight years, I was bounded in chains
Now I've found my master and he has set me free
He taught me to pray, and he taught me to dance to the rhythm of
angels song
He listens and watches with Pilgrims of barren land.

Now that I have gained my freedom at last
I can see the moonlight in the sky at night
And I can go to the park and play
Then say farewell to those awesome chains.

SOLDIERS

With all the trees and stones along,
Earth is trembling when soldiers sing:
   'We the soldiers are there for war
   and be prepared to have our spar.'

So be quick to make your spar;
Off in danger, off in war we roam,
'Forward in the wilderness we sigh and moan'
While earth is trembling when comrades charge.

At the twilight of the evening
And at the dawn of the morning;
We, the comrades will remember them
Some may not live to be coming home
But we who survive must soldier on.

War is bad no matter how near or far,
War is sad and still we have to spar or die;
For by sparring is the way we can survive;
While earth trembles when soldiers sing.

CLIMB THE MOUNTAIN

I will climb the highest mountain,
I will echo from the highest peak;
That I have got my freedom at last.
I have worked for this for many a year,
Now I am released and I am free
The years I spent in that morbid prison
Have me to view this world in a different light;
Then view the people in their plight.
I will shout from the highest mountain,
I will proclaim from the highest peak:
I am now a 'People's President'
Free at last, free at last, we are free,
We have gained our freedom
And now we are free.

WOMAN SUCCESS

The heights that women reach just now,
Was not obtained by sudden flight,
For they were sewing the seeds to reap
The reward they need to reach the top,
They find it hard to fill their days
For the goal the one they want to reach,
Now that they have reached the top
We all will prosper in a booming world.
Now that they are equal to the man
They are not inferior anymore
They strive to get the things they want
For it is scarce when they are not around
Now that they have reached the top
They demand the respect they never have
For women usually sow the seeds,
For Men to have something to eat,
They will suppress the speech they have in mind
For the Men are not sure,
When they have to listen to the woman
That always be housebound.
Happy are they that reach the top
For they will be there for a long, long time.
High are their titles, gracious are their names
For they have worked so hard to achieve
The things they have done to reach the top.

GIVE US

Give us masses of wit and wisdom,
Give us love that never ceases,
Give us patience to abide,
Give us peace that never ends,
Give us grace to see thy face,
Give us blessings in abundance,
Give us rain to water our crops,
Let it be pure and safe to drink.
Give us freedom of our birth,
Give us light in this darkened cloud,
Give us sanctity oh caring Lord,
Bind us with love, hope and faith
And let this earth be safe and sound.

LONDON

When I get to London
I shall sing and shout
When I get there
The river Thames will rise
When she hears me singing my songs
For I'm now in London Town.
Let the hills and valley echo
The sweetest sound when given a chance
For I'm now in London Town.

London 'Oh London' the home of Bureaucrat
London 'Oh London' the home of the free!
'Praise to those who made it be'
There is no other place like London?
For we'll have our freedom here
'Twas what we believe in that makes us great
So we'll go on to mightier stakes
I'll stress there's no other place like London
For it is the home for the humble and noble.

HAVE WE FORGOTTEN

Have we forgotten that we are parents,
In this land where crimes prevail,
And fills us with grief, guilt and fear?
The killing of a young child,
Sends shivers down the spine of parents everywhere.

Every time a new one is killed or raped,
We ask 'Why did this happen?'
The blunt answer is we caused it.
We have failed to discipline our children
In their early stages in life;
We allowed them to get away with things,
Which normally are not allowed;
We forgot to teach them the basic things in life,
The difference between right and wrong
To respect authority and its elders.

We must admit that sometimes we are living
In a hopeless zone.
No work, no hope, no faith, no love,
Poverty and drugs have taken their toll,
Are the government, the schools, the churches
Or society to be blamed?
We too as parents can't drift away from our responsibilities,
We are equally to be blamed for not being
An inspiration to our children.

Grandparents have a lot to offer if given a chance,
So seek them out, for the more the better.
Politicians, church ministers, teachers
And people in high places must set an example,
We need you to be an inspiration to our children.

FREEDOM AT LAST

Yippee! Yippee! Ah! We got our freedom
Now we can proclaim from the roof top
That we are free! Free! Free!

Freedom at last! Freedom at last!
Yippee! Yippee! We can have a mind of our own
And share the things we own.

Freedom to walk the streets at night,
Freedom to go to dance alright
And freedom to have a vote insight.

Yippee! Yippee! Oh! We can learn academics,
We can go to the park and play
And we can go to the bath and swim.
Freedom! Freedom! We are free
And we can proclaim our freedom.

BLESSED

How blessed am I to have a caring Mum,
How blessed am I to have a caring Dad,
How blessed am I to have a loving family,
How blessed am I to do the things I've done,
How blessed am I to see the world as it is:
How blessed am I to have water, food and shelter
How blessed am I in time of trial and grief
To feel the presence of our majesty,
When I cross the wilderness in distress.
His majesty's presence is always here to guide me
In the darkest days caused by the human race.
When in distress to Him I call of Him my rescue came
Then I will view this world and the inhabitants
In the clearest vision ever given to one.
'How blessed am I to have a vision so bright'
For I can see aliens coming to light;
I will look beyond the horizon and sing the tunes,
'Our majesty will welcome and adore.'
How blessed am I to go to Him in peace
From the east I will rise up and praise his name
For He is so blessed a Father to me.

LOOK WHAT HE'S DONE

Look what he's done in my house
He took my wife out for a meal
Then he came back to make a deal
Look what he's done in my house.

Look what he's done to my song
He changes the words, he changes the tune
Look what he's done to my song

Look what he's done to my name
He commits his fraud, he commits his crime
He uses my name to cover his fault
Look what he's done to my name

He was sent to jail, but I'm outside
'Now look' what he's done to himself
And look what he's done to me.

EARTH IS SHIVERING

With all the ice and snow along
Earth is shivering as we sing our song.
Give us warmth we sigh and moan
Let us have warmth for human gladness.
Remember when we went to play
We were told how to cope with cold spell in winter months.

Some may die perhaps in freezing weather,
If they've not, prepare to wear much clothes.
Give them warm clothes for human comfort
Let us preserve wool for human gladness
While earth is shivering with awesome coldness.

Remember little birds when we left our food
For they are shivering in blistering coldness
And can't find a seed in snowy weather.

WINTER SPRING SUMMER AND AUTUMN

Now that winter chill is going,
And the bright spring is near,
All the birds will be singing
To know the berries soon will ripe.
The hedgehogs will soon be crawling,
For the warm spell is drawing near.
The squirrels will be climbing
Knowing the trees will soon have nuts.
Men and women will soon be bathing
In the pool and in the sun.
The children will be playing,
In the park and in their garden.
Alas! Autumn leaves are golden,
And autumn leaves are falling,
Autumn rain is pouring
And autumn wind is blowing.

DRUGS

Do not take drugs
For it will make you sick,
Do not take drugs
For it will not make you tick,
Drugs are bad and it makes you sad.

People sell drugs to make a buck
And you'll find yourself being stuck.
They are simply trying to mess you up
That's when you'll realise it is a slip up.

Sellers of drugs are evil
If you take it you will be a devil.
Drugs can be good at times,
If administered by a physician.

It eases the pain, the anxieties and pressures of life
Say no, to your friends who introduce you to drugs.

NIGHT AND DAY

Remember your day is my night
While my night is your day,
My darkness is your light
While my light is your darkness.

Our day and our night are just as important
As our darkness and our light.

When moon and stars brighten the sky,
The earth and its inhabitants are fast asleep
And when the sun shines on planet earth
Humans, animals and every living thing will all be at play.

Perhaps the fish will search for prey
In pure crystal water, while they the hunter
May become the hunted
For sharks and crocodiles will search for flavour.

WHERE ARE YOU

Width as wide as the ocean,
Depth as deep as the sea,
Blue as bright as the sky above
Where is Heaven and where are you?
'Are You where the rose tree grows?'
The one that climbs along the wall
With fragrant smell across the lawn,
Oh Where! Oh where! are You?
I saw Your footprints across the sand
And heard You whisper through the wind.
A chance to love I have
'A chance to glorify Your presence.'
A never dying love to share
And will see it in the sky.
Width as wide as the ocean
Depth as deep as the sea
Oh share with me the depth of love
For in Your arms I cling,
To share Your love and grace
And say thanks to my Father and King
And glorify your precious name.
'Help me to sing and pray,'
As I walk this path alone;
With trembling hands and trembling feet
I saw Your footprints in the sand;
'I know You are here,' but cannot see Your face
'Your love is like the diamond that shines on snow'
Your presence is like the sun that shines through the mirror;
Oh where! Oh where! Oh where! Are You?
I am safe beneath Your love and care
And will sing and dance and I'll watch and pray
And sanctify Your glorious name.

SURVIVING SQUIRREL

Behold the squirrel on the fence
Playing with the leaves that fall,
On the meadow one frosty morning
With the light breeze blowing west.
She swishes her tail and ruffles her hair
To keep her warm as she rushes along.
The nuts are scarce, the ground so hard
We wonder how she survives at all.
Matters seem worst when cat's about
So she'll be prepared for the great escape.
The strangest thing about the cat,
Is the way she tries to catch her tail;
She is so agile when she climbs the wall
We wonder why she does not fall.

CRACKING WALLS

We walk the streets and lane along,
While walls are cracking under awesome song;
We, the Christians are here to sing
While atheists twitch and turn their rings.

Under the roof we sing and clap,
While the cathedral is cracking under awesome song.
Remember when we went to church?
We were told we have to search!
For love and friendship from our Maker.

Down on the road they search for prey,
While walls are cracking under awesome song;
And angels listen in glee as we sing along.

CALL ME

Call me and I'll be there to welcome you,
Call me and I'll be there to comfort you;
Call me and I'll be there to see you through.

Call me when the rain starts pouring
Call me when the wind starts blowing.
Call me when you are in distress
Call me and I'll be there to rescue you.

Call me when the money starts coming
Call me, just keep calling
For I'll be there to love, love, love.

You can call on my name
For you know wherever you are
I'll be there to cling, cling, cling,
Just keep calling, I'll be there to love, love, love.

CAN WE NOT SEE

Can we not see that others are crying,
Can we not see that others are wailing!
Can we not see the pain in their eyes.

Can we not see they are in distress,
Can we not see they are oppressed,
Can we not see they are on the brink
Of life and death.

Can we not see they have no food,
Can we not see they have no water;
Can we not see they have no fire.

Can we not see they have no freedom,
Can we not see they have no wisdom;
Can we not see they are not wise.

We have to change our selfish attitude
By giving them freedom and a multitude of courage.

I LOVE YOU MY DARLNG

I love you my darling,
At night when I go to bed;
I think of you and I cry.

I want you to touch me
I want you to caress me,
Hold me, squeeze me, love me.

Breathe on me, breath of life,
Breathe on me, breathe on me
As deep as you can.

Hold me, hold me, hold me,
Squeeze me, squeeze me, squeeze me,
Kiss me, kiss me, kiss me.

Sing to me, smile with me
Dance, dance, dance with me.

IF

If I have a pen, I'll write in the morning,
I'll write in the evening and at twilight;
The lyrics with passionate words.

If I have a pen I'll write in the afternoon,
I'll write in the daytime and at dawn;
The words with lyrics as passionate as you.

If I have a pen, I'll write my lines,
I'll write in the room and in my closet;
The notes with passionate lines to massage your heart.

If I have a pen, I'll write my memoirs,
My memoirs will make your heart beat faster;
Especially when it is congratulating you.

The pen I want must be a golden one,
To write the thrill I got from you.

AUTUMN

Autumn leaves are golden,
Autumn leaves are falling,
Autumn wind is blowing,
And autumn rain is pouring.
For weeks no sun has shone
Each passing day goes by
A woman told me
That the leaves at the lake are dry.

Now that autumn will soon be ended
And the dark winter is near
All the squirrels are busy hiding
The nuts from the trees.
In the park and in their larder,
The hedgehog will be at rest
In the dry leaves along the hedge
Hallowe'en night will soon be coming
All the witches will be gliding
On their broomstick and on their pumpkins.
Guy Fawkes night will soon be here
Where the children burn their dummies
On the bonfire in their garden
They roast the bangers and beefburgers
Then sing their songs
And shout away with the guy.

LITTLE DREAMER

Dream my little one, dream my pretty one
Under the canopy you have your slumber!
Sleep – will fill your magical dreams.
Midnight dreams of solemn hour may come
To hasten your heart of love and pleasure;
You may hear the voice of angels singing,
And with joy their heart may rejoice at your endeavour,
Let the angels dance in glee at your request
You are having your magical dreams;
How triumphant when the angels see
You are having the dream in your favour.
How exciting the dawn of day is breaking,
The cocks are crowing, the donkeys braying;
And hence goes the angels in your dreams.

POEMS

I would like to be a poet,
To write poems all day long
Poems of joy, poems of grief
Poems of laughter and echoing
From this heart of mine
Poems are written by fools like me
But only God can make me write.
I'll write you a poem
Of that beautiful land where
I'll be writing that La-La Bye,
You and me, me and you,
Will write together all day long
Poems are written by fools like me
But only God can make me write.
I'll write you a poem
About the birds and the bees,
That will make me so great.
Thanks for the privilege,
While I'll enjoy the victory,
Poems are written by fools like me
But only God can make me write.

SOMEONE TO LOVE

You'll be happy for someone to love
Now that you found me I'll never let you go;
I hope you realise you'll be the only one,
My love you will call all your own.

You just listen to my heartbeat
And you'll know how much I care
Your charm is so graceful
No wonder you're so beautiful;
You are amazing and so faithful
With a voice as eloquent like an angel.
Do breathe on me my darling dear!
Breathe on me as deep as you can.
You and I can be prophets for our love
And may the passionate love between us grow.

GREAT

Great is the mighty valour,
Great is the music and dance,
Great is the celestial house,
Great is His precious name;
How great it is to be loved by You.
How great when the tyrants fallen
How great are the wisdom of our people;
Great are the mighty oaks,
Great are the fish in this wonderful sea,
Great are the people of this beautiful world.
Great, great to You Your Majesty.
Great are the people who listen
To the shows of great heroes,
Great spirits are the Supremacy of this wonderful world.
How great it is to be loved by You.
The Lord is great his presence of everlasting peace
Brings joy to our hearts,
Great, great to You Your Majesty,
Great! Great! Great! Are the wisdom of great people.

WE

We the luckiest of all creatures,
We the strangest of them all;
We the enemies of the world
And the cleverest of its kind,
Yet we watch without protest
As our society degenerates.
We have failed to teach our children
The basics of morality,
We have allowed them, to molest our neighbours
'Then stood idly by and did nothing.'
Now we are seeing the evil flourishing,
Some murdered, some battered, some robbed,
'We the observer of the world,'
'Have got the planet in our stride.'
And have to put the bad things right,
'That we can have a little pride'
We the changers of the world,
Have changed the goodness of our being,
And now we are living in a war torn world
Sadly, slowly, quietly and meekly
'We are realising our mistakes'
For not disciplining our children.

DECLARE AND SWEAR

Auntie Mary declare
Uncle Charlie swear,
Under the moon and stars
They bow down and declare
They need their freedom
And they need their share.

OH WHAT A BEAUTIFUL LOVE

Oh what a beautiful, beautiful love
My darling has for me,
Oh what a beautiful, beautiful love
My darling has for me;
Pretty, pretty as the roses, sweet, sweet as honey
High, high as the mountain above
There's love for me,
Oh what a wonderful, wonderful love
My darling has for me
Pretty, pretty as the roses, sweet, sweet as honey
High, high as the mountain above
There's love for me.

SINCE WINE

Since wine is a healthy drink, serve on!
Give me more and more of it,
Fill my glass, let it run over and over,
Let me drink of it, for it is healthy.

How good, this drink of wine I have?
For I'm feeling healthy, and full of strength
Give me wine, to bring out the best
Let me drink of it, for it is healthy.

Wine and dine me in your home,
Let it be safe and pure to drink;
The wine from your vineyard in your yard,
These that are made from finest grapes;
Will let me feel healthy
Wealthy and wise.

WHEN LIFE

When life is full of anxiety
And life is full of tears
Don't waste precious time moaning
Just seek salvation from above.

When everyone forsakes you
You make sure they are loved
It got no secrets for them to hear
The limit of expression they will see.

Love is so genuine it can light a fire
It defuses to the horrible gas we breathe
And make it pure and free from germ
It is like the measles we have only once.

When I consider life is all a cheat,
Some make it profitable at others' expense.
Lay not your trust in a tongue twisted soul
But aim for love with someone who cares.

WHEN I FALL IN LOVE

When I fall in love a maiden I never want
For all I want is a virgin to educate.

I can only fall in love at the dawn of day
When the cocks are crowing, the donkeys are braying
I will be wooing,
Wooing for the lover of my life
Falling in love is like the dewdrops on a thirsty plant
Which will be enough to sustain the roots.

When I fall in love, it will be an adventure
Something I want to explore!

When I fall in love, I will be like a butterfly
Roaming on the meadow,
So carefree, I just want all to see my pretty wings,
My companions treasure most.

When I fall in love I'll know the only thing that's stronger is
Death

Oh life where is my love?
Oh love where is my victory?
It is all wrapped up between you and me.

SINCE APPLE

Since apple is the fruit of love, eat on
Pick one, pick two, pick many more
Let us eat of it for it is love

Remember the story of Adam and Eve
Eve picked an apple then gave it to Adam
Adam ate of it then realised he was naked
From then on sleaze has begun.

Was this the discovery of the fruit of love?
Or is it the love for the fruit that apples bring,
Pick one, pick two, pick many more.

Since apple is the fruit of love, eat on!
Give us more and more of it
Let us eat of it, for it is love
But only from the same tree in one's garden.

THE TRUTH

The truth that we know which concerns us
Is usually just half spoken, in case repeated.
The truth usually comes up at the last moment
The truth of a Politician is always distorted,
But many come out if challenged by an opposition.

The truth is never often said by the devil
Sometimes truth is always a lie to them
The meaning of the word truth is never
In the vocabulary of the devil.
Every truth must be tampered with
For the evil one will not be satisfied.

'The truth is good, for good is truth'
'God is truth, for the truthful'
He blesses those who speak the truth.

Let the truth be told wherever we are,
Let the truth be told whatever the case
Truth is blessed, and one is blessed for speaking the truth
And that will come from 'The Great Superior'.

NURSERY RHYME

Slowly, silently and curiously
We gather up the hedgehogs
Prickles will hurt our fingers
But their fleas cannot bite us.

HARD TIMES

Come on everyone
Listen to my words,
Listen and I will tell you
That times are getting harder
So we'll have to make a larder.

In every corner we stroll
We can hear everyone saying,
We can store our grain
That we can eat when it rains.

One thing we must acknowledge,
That our reaping soon begins;
Where we gather up the crops
To feed our flocks and our folks
And say farewell to hard times.

NURSERY RHYME

You got fame
You got no shame,
You bare your bot
And that is bad,
You feel cool
You are no fool.

NURSERY RHYME

Sour sop, sweet sop
Jam and honey,
Birds and insects
Buy without money.

NURSERY RHYME

Bow-wow, bow-wow where have you been?
I've been to my master's meadow
To look for his flocks,
The night was dark and they were all right
So I left them sleeping and chewing their cud.

NURSERY RHYME

Pretty Polly dressed as a dolly
In her lady's raiment;
Said Miss Molly to Pretty Polly,
Can I have your garment?
Said Pretty Polly to Miss Molly
You can have my raiment.

NURSERY RHYME

When you need a chop
Come to my shop
My chop is the best
Better than all the rest.

NURSERY RHYME

Just the job for Bob,
Just the one for a bob,
He'll be fit for the job
And he will earn my bob.
Isn't it funny
How times have changed;
No more job for Bob
You sit and mope
No wonder you sob, sob, sob.

OH MIRANDA

Oh Miranda, Oh Miranda,
Where did you eat last night?
The wind was so strong
The journey was so rough
I slept at my lover's camp.
Don't ask me why, I'm here tonight,
For I'll be eating at Aunt Nellie's café:
'I'll put on some weight'
To have a bit more strength
To motivate the dancers
As I do the rocking and rolling,
'You'll love me tonight,'
For I'll be alright
To rock around the room all night.

CAT FROM DOWN THE ROAD

I am the cat from down the road,
That catches the rats outside your door:
I'm ready when rats are there,
When they see me they disappear,
I'll sever them at the dawn of day
From me they are never safe.
In the evening's dimming light,
I'm the assassin day and night;
Life seems pressured when dogs are there,
But I'll be safe when they've gone to sleep.
'Remember I'm the cat from down the road.'
That catches the rat from your door,
So leave some milk on the mat
For I'll be there to catch the rat.

THINGS WE LOVE

We love the golden leaves on trees
When autumn breeze is nigh,
Grand Papa preparing the meadow
For winter is drawing near.

We love to listen to Top of the Pops
When musicians are playing their tunes,
With singers singing their songs
And the dancing in the hall.

We love the moonlight on the veranda
With golden glow on the window,
The silence in the house nearby
All sleeping on the couch.

WATCHING AND LOVING ME

Someone in this hall is watching me,
Someone in this hall is loving me,
Someone in this hall is helping me.

Someone, somewhere in everyone's eye
Have got a crush on me;
Mighty you, powerful you, amazing you
Have all the wonderful things in sight,
Of human thoughts and everything
To enrich the heart of a humble soul.

Someone in this hall is so dear to me,
Someone in this hall is making me tall;
Someone in this hall is massaging my heart.

There's happy faces everywhere
Smiling ones, laughing ones and suggestive ones;
Emotionally taken up by your loving presence,
Caressing the hearts as the hour ticks away;
How many hearts at random sent
Have broken the chain that seldom bent,
Someone, somewhere, is everyone's friend.

ONE SUNNY DAY

One sunny day when my task is over
I'll fly away to a land of Paradise
Where there's love and tranquillity.

This Paradise land is far, far away
From human thoughts of everything
Where only birds and angels sing.

Far, far away in the wilderness I'll go
To see the angels dance on snow
In a rhythm never observed before.

When the moon shines on the snowy ground
I'll be singing sweet songs of joy
To the birds and angels in Paradise.
Will Paradise lost be Paradise gained
For I'll be laughing for my praise.

CELESTIAL SONG

For all the hills and valleys along,
Earth is echoing into celestial song;
We the singers are to cheer
And the angels will stand and stare.
We will die perhaps in war so far,
If we stop singing our celestial song.
Onward into the hills we roam
Forward into the valley we moan.
Give us victory to Earth's gladness
Let us echo songs of awesome goodness.
Remember when we went to war
Everyone will have to spar,
Off in danger, off in battle we roam
Onward on our knees we rattle and moan,
When earth echoes into celestial song.

ENOUGH

Enough of the muck of blasphemy,
Enough of the false way of worshipping,
Enough of the worshipping of idols,
Enough of the evil doers,
Enough of the persecution of Christians,
Enough of the abuse of our children,
Enough of the abuse of our women,
Enough of racial discrimination,
Enough of the grovelling to the bureaucrats,
Enough of the rocking and the rolling,
Enough of the odour of sleaze,
Enough of the evil in our society,
It is enough our struggle soon shall see,
The love of Jesus whispers hope and peace within.

FOUR SEASONS

Now that winter chill is going
And the bright green spring is near,
All the birds will soon be singing
Sweet, ripe fruits will soon be here,
The sleepy hedgehogs soon be waking,
Summer's spell is drawing near,
Men and women soon sunbathing
By the pool and on the beach,
Children play in summer clothing
In the park and in the garden.
'Alas! Green leaves will soon be golden'
And golden leaves will be falling.
Autumn rain starts pouring,
And autumn wind is blowing.

THE RICH AND FAMOUS

I heard you speak of the better place
Where your parents used to live.
Along the olive trees in the sunny slopes,
High above the valley of blowing wind.
'The awesome houses of the rich and famous'
Where fragrant flowers perfume the wind
And strange-colour birds with flapping wings
It's all there, it's all there, my humble child.
For years we have seen this my little one,
Decades have passed with deep music of joy,
'This is how the rich and famous live'
High above the valley of blowing wind,
With fame, power and riches
For that's the way the rich and famous live.

CRICKET GLORIOUS CRICKET

Cricket glorious cricket
Brian Lara at the test,
Brian Lara made his best
With a cut above the rest.
Brian hits them for six
He had them asking for more and more.
Although he is left-handed
Brian is a king.

He's a king for the matches
He is the best for he is blessed
Brian Lara, everyone shouts!
Brian Lara, Brian Lara!
Give us more, give us more.
Garfield did his best
But Brian beat the best,
He plays his matches
And hits balls for fours and sixes.

PASSING SEASONS

Now that summer has passed,
And autumn leaves are golden;
All the leaves will soon have fallen
For winter is drawing near.

Squirrels are busy hiding the nuts
For cold spells they cannot trust.
Many birds will migrate to faraway places
To have their berries and sing their praises.
Hedgehogs will soon be hiding
In the dry leaves along the hedge.
Witches will soon be flying
On their broomsticks around their pumpkins,
Children will soon be burning
The dummies they name Guy Fawkes.
Santa Claus will soon be wearing
That beautiful red robe when greeting the young.

They gave the children little toys
To celebrate the festive time.
Snow may fall on Christmas day
To make this day a fairy way,
Mary had this little child and he is here to stay.

He follows us everywhere we go,
For He will guide us as we play;
He is here within us for He is
Christ for us.

LABELLED AS AN ANGEL

'You are an angel,' they proclaimed,
How many of us can be labelled as one?
Yes, you are an angel for everyone is saying so.

You walk like an angel,
You talk like an angel,
You are as graceful as an angel.
Your colourful pattern wings have left
The nation gasping at your Heavenly motion:
Heaven knows you are such a motivator.

We shall be listening for your music in the air,
Will it sound like a violin,?
Or as the timbrel or the harp?
We shall be dancing to your music and song,
When the twilight is drawing nigh.

I CRIED

I cried because I'm happy
I cried because I'm sad
I cried because I want to cry
For you to know, I have my freedom.

I cried great tears of joy
I cried because I saw an incredible force being brought to light
To see people from the East
Gaining forces with people from the West;
I looked beyond the cloud and smiled
For I can see friendship from a mile;
Then wonder why was it necessary to cry.

Crying is the expression of the poor and humble
So is it for the high and noble;
I cried for my people in distress
I cried to my 'maker' for in distress to 'Him' I called
From 'Him' my endeavours came
I looked beyond the clouds and smile;
Then I wonder why was it necessary to cry.

THINGS I LOVE IN BRIXTON

I love the lights of Brixton
Red apples on the stall
The Rastafarians in their coloured caps
The talking of patois on the street.

I love the lights of Brixton
The bright colours in the store
Hot patties in the West Indian shops
The nibbling down the road.

I love the lights of Brixton
Tube station up the road
The lack of silence everywhere
All human life is there.

EMBRACE

For all the power and looks you have
I am waiting to see you smile
So I am finding it hard to concentrate.

Every thought and every word is lost
In that embrace I missed most
So hold me close my darling dear
You glitter like a diamond in my ring
You are just like the dewdrops on a thirty plant

'Twas at the dawn of the day I thought of you
then at twilight you were here embracing my lips with love.

Give me much love as you can
Then I'll embrace you with my warm and caring thought
Every breath I took I remember you
For you are the light in this darkest room.

GOD IS

God is power and God is might
God is good and God is great;
God is Mum and not a nun,
God is Dad and not a monk;

'God is God, for He is the God;'
God creates the trees and creates the light,
He creates you and He creates me,
'That is why He is the God'.

God is powerful and yet so pure
He answers our prayers
But does not say yes, as we would like,
'He is slow to answer and swift to act.'

God is where, we know not when,
When in distress, to Him we call,
'From Him our rescue come,'
We seek His love to answer our plight,
That we can have everlasting peace.

HOLD BACK THE YEARS

Your hair is grey, but not with years,
You were born with many at your birth.
The summer has passed and with it
Came the temptation to ignore the advice
By constant tanning oneself in the sun.

You have the skin that always looks tanned
And I'm always asking if that's the wonder of the sun.

We may marvel at the fragile beauties
Those that baked themselves in the sun
Will find oneself with more and more unwanted skin.

Since the ozone is in sight,
The sun is hardly a tonic for the skin,
You'll hold back the years and your chin
To tell the wonder of a youthful you.

GO TELL IT ON THE MOUNTAIN

Go tell it on the mountain,
That a child is born today;
Go shout it from the valley
That goodness is here to stay.

Go tell the villagers that Christ is born today.
Wise men will be there
Carrying gold, frankincense and myrrh
These are gifts to our newborn King.

Mary had this little child,
'Of whom the fruit of glory lies.'
In her tender arms He laid,
Gently sleeping in the manger.

Rejoice, rejoice, the church bell rings,
Our Saviour is born in Bethlehem.

LOOK

Look down on us our Saviour Lord
Look down and help us as we cry in vain,
Our tears will not dry until we are free,
Not because of our colour, or because of our being
Why we are the victims of this uncaring world.

'We saw the violence on the street'
We saw the victim fighting for life,
We saw the oppressor released and set free
We saw, what we saw, and what we saw,
Was a violent crime.

Oh! Look down us our Saviour and save us from sin
'How many are to die, how many are to lie
Where is the justice? Where are the judges?
When will there be freedom for the children you adore?

Oh! Look down on us Lord as we mourn in vain,
We are Your children and we are in pain,
'We look for Your guidance to set us free.'

HOMELESS AND HUNGRY

Crying for help and crying in pain,
They are homeless, hungry and insane.
Shaking with cold and feeling pain
Their pride is gone, they've submitted
To ultimate shame.

Begging for food, water and shelter,
Have become the words they've spoken most
Help them please, they begged in vain
They are cold, hungry and feeling pain.
They pitifully held their hands to people passing by
Begging endlessly as the hours ticked away.

Trembling hands, shaking body, wobbly feet,
Runny nose, bloodshot, sunken eyes;
They tried to gain their pride
By gazing beyond the human faces,
Trying to stop their tears falling.
Help them please they begged in pain,
They have fallen from grace and there's no gain.
Will society develop a morbid sense of guilt
As well as sensitive attitude towards their plight?
Help them please, before they fall,
Segregation and degradation have taken their toll
Their plight is endless and we have been told.

SEVEN WORDS OF FOUR LETTERS

Hate
Fear
Kill
L
O
V
E
Envy
Loss
Lies

How can these seven words have such effects on our lives?
Let awesome love divide them all.
When there's love there's no pain,
'So we'll play on the plain.'

Love changes everything:
For the rich, the poor and the humble.
Let the power of love remove that hate
Let the power of love remove that fear,
Let the power of love remove that envy
And let the power of love restore that loss.

Let us only kill to eat,
For when we're full of everything
There's no time for us to lie.

COME TOGETHER

Come together, come together just now
You can love us, you can love us now
When we get together, who can come between us/
Love can save us just now
So forget the hatred, deceit and envy.
'Love can bind us together,' bind us together in love!
Let the hills and valleys, rocks and mountains come forward
For the perfect love we're putting together
This perfect love, this never ending love
Will find a way in all human hearts.

When the thunder clap and the earth quake
We shall be embracing under the canopy of love
Let the earth bring forth her increase
With all this love we have to share.

YOU ARE MY HIGH FLYER

You are a high flyer do you know?
You are a high flyer they told me so
You are the high flyer we're yearning for.

You are the high flyer in my life
You are the high flyer in my world
You are the high flyer in my mind.

You are the high flyer in every event
Make no mistake, this is your beefstake
You can tell there's gossip everywhere.

You are the high flyer we adore
You are the high flyer of that I'm sure
You are the high flyer we were waiting for,
My! Oh my! You're flying high
Always be successful, as time goes by.

COME DOWN

Come down, come down and fill
Our hearts with your love
Since You revealed to us Your presence
I know we are not alone
You are guiding us to victory.

May our days be merry and bright
Just like that precious day
You took us from captivity
And taught us the way to salvation
For this we will always sing your praises.

My mama taught me to love and respect You
That's why I'm always singing praises to you
Let us echo a song for sweet deliverance
When the cathedral bell rings for our coming.

On our bending knees we shall sing and pray
For we are Pilgrims carrying a banner
And hoping for others to join our band.

Cleanse our hearts from doubt and fear
And let Your divine love come shining through
For You are One and One for all.

QUOTATIONS

1.   If I am wronged by anyone I cannot wait to tell the world,
      But if they are wronged by me I would hide behind the
      wind, then hoping it will blow away.

2.   Tell not your troubles to everyone for it may come back
      to haunt you, for some people thrive on causing pain.

3.   Never tell a colourful lie, tell a colourless one, for a
      colourless one is no lie at all.

4.   I would like an honours degree of my heart on morals for
      when I have that no one can take that away from me.

5.   Take my purse take my keys and my possessions but
      never rob me of my freedom and my virginity.

6.   Never go trouble hunting, if you haven't an insurance, for
      I'll sue your pants off you.

7.   Be kind to those who are unkind then watch the grin on
      their faces.

8.   When I marry my husband, I will never have my best
      friend again, for after a while that best friend may
      become my worst enemy for running away with my
      husband.

9.   Suffering is mainly caused when there is no
      understanding and wisdom.

PSALMS OF PRAISE

When the rain is pouring
And the earth is quaking
I'll sing psalms of praises
For I'll be inside looking out.

When all the trees on every bank
Echo songs of sweetest praises
When raindrops are massaging their roots
And will enable ripe fruits to appear
Singing birds sing their songs
Singing praises for sweet ripe berries.

Women dressed in summer clothing
Picking berries for sweet jam tarts
Men and children are ready to eat
The sweet tart that women baked.

When the rain stops pouring
And the earth stops quaking
I'll stop singing Psalms of Praises
Then eat the fruits that harvest brings.

'Twas what we eat that makes us great
So I'll go on to mightier stakes
And sing my songs of Psalms with Praises.

FAILING LOVE

Have you ever watched the one you love
Gradually drifting away from you;
All hope, all faith, all respect is gone,
Lies, lies and more lies is mainly the cause.

Malicious lies, and awesome lies
Has left a hole in a human's heart
Growing older, growing wiser, growing graceful
And cannot tolerate this brutality any more.
Heaven knows I am at a crossroad.

I should have seen this long ago,
Love did conquer lies and that was great
Now it has gone and that's a shame
Sorrow and despair has taken its toll
With sleepless nights and anxiety in bed.

WINE

'Twas where the vine with grapes creep along,
When earth is singing a harmonised song;
'We, the boozers are here to drink'
The wine made from grapes in our vineyard.

Perhaps some may drink a bottle or two?
Then wonder when to find a vacant loo.
Give them wine to earth's gladness?
Let them echo sounds of gracious goodness.

Some may have a fit of endless laughter!
While earth is singing a harmonised song?
Give them wine to bring out the best!
Let them drink from the west.

East is east and west is west,
'But who cares where is the best?'

UP IN SPACE

Out of this world and up in space
This is the journey the astronauts choose
High above the sky they'll go
To mighty heights on outer space
They'll only stop when they reach their destination
Which is cast into discovery's deepest shadow.
They will look back at this world
They left below and wonder what
A wonderful beautiful sight.

HARMONIOUS SONG

From all the roads and lane along,
Earth is echoing into harmonious song:
We, the children, are to cheer,
While the teachers will stand and steer.

We may win a prize in October,
If the musicians will have a gig in September.

Away into the hall we'll sing and dance,
Down on the floor we'll rock and roll;
Holding hands as we jig along,
When playing our harmonious song.

We, the children will clap and sing,
While the teachers will rock and roll;
Clapping our hands in great amusement
While earth is echoing into harmonious song.

ANGELS WATCH

Slowly and silently I'll go to bed
Placing the pillow under my head,
Then saying a prayer to my God.

Isn't it nice to sigh and sleep
And ask the Lord my soul to keep,
Then ask His protection while I rest.

In the evening's dimming light,
I am a motivator day and night,
Yet angels watch me while I dream.

I will sleep until dawn of day
Till the monkeys are ready to bray
And the cub begins her play.

Facing East I'll slowly wake
To watch the sun start to make
His daily journey to the West.

THE WAY YOU SING

I like the way you sing your song
It makes me want to dance along;
You sing your song of peace and love
It makes me feel I'm in Heaven above.
Open your vocals, sing loud and clear
Let your voice be heard far and near.
Your voice sounds just like the violin
And cymbals, harps and drums and things.
At dawn we hear the song of birds
If only you could know their words
Only you could sing their song;
And help the world to understand.
Think of the nightingale, the thrush
The robin in the highest bush.
The silent wind whistling through the trees
The murmuring brook flowing over the lees;
Your song means so much to my ears
To treasure through the ensuing years.

RUSHING WIND

The rushing wind that is so strong,
The sail that pushes the boat along;
With flowing water pure and clear
Makes sounds that echo far and near.
The shining sun with golden beam,
The silver water with softer gleam;
Is with us as we sail and sing our song
And will help us to relax as we sail along.
A few centuries ago we depended on you
To push the ships across the ocean blue.

You blew my hat from off my head
And heard you whisper when I was in bed.
Blowing wind and rushing wind
Restless wind and careless wind
Will carry love to this garden of mine
Which will pollinate the spruce and the pine.

OUR CHILDREN WITH CRIME

Our children with crime, and out of control
Our children with drugs and a mouth of abusive words
Our children are causing pain and concern.

They swing violently on dangerous paths,
Then looking anxiously over their shoulders
Wondering when to make their escape.

Dressed in oversized clothes, so soft and baggy
Will fill their pockets with the drugs and ciggies
Then swing violently on dangerous paths.

Are our children the product of the swinging sixties?
Or are they the product of the video in motion
Nobody knows, but those are to blame.

Open your hearts, you children of ours
You need our support, and you need our love
You can be crime free, and be in control.

GOODNESS

When Goodness goes marching on
I would like to be in that number
For Goodness is marching is on.

Tell my mama and papa
I won't be there for very long
For Goodness is on their way
And they are singing melodious songs

Tell all the people to prepare
For Goodness is on their way
And need their love and their say
Then we'll go on to mightier stakes

Far from home into the road we roam
Searching for Goodness to be our friend
And searching for love we never have
Then say farewell to our darkest days.

They are marching on, they are marching on,
So let us join this happy band
We'll clap our hands and sing for joy
And join Goodness for they are marching on.

THE SKY AT NIGHT

I looked above the trees one night
Then wondered why the stars so bright
In great amazement, I saw a shadow
Way above the clouds of moving wind.

I was so bewildered I called my friend
Just one look at that shadow I said
Gasping with delight and yet so frightened to say
It looks like our father from above.

Was He wondering where we've gone wrong?
Or was He admiring the beautiful fruits that our harvest brings
The Millennium is just a whisper away
So maybe He is admiring our dome
Or was He just fascinated by our gnomes?

Strange things happen in the sky at nights
So wait for Him to ride the clouds
He loves His children who obey His rules
And He also loves an invitation to our hearts
Just keep a watch on the sky at nights
For we'll never know when He's in sight.

MY BABY

My baby is out of the country,
My baby is out of the town,
My baby is sailing, forever sailing
Across the ocean blue.

Go! Shout it from the mountain
I want my baby back home.

My baby, my baby my little bonny babe,
You are my lover in this our world;
You taught me to laugh
You brought me to tears
When you sing as only you can.

Please bring my baby back home to me,
Push the boat as fast as you can;
For my baby is whinging and pining for love
Go, bring my baby back home to me.

My baby is coming, my baby is laughing,
My baby is longing to be back home;
Alas my babe is coming soon
So we'll be off to the country town.

BABIES SONG

We walk the streets with prams along,
When babies are singing a cheerful song;
We as parents are listening in glee
To hear our babies singing a melodious song.

Perhaps we'll buy them some tinky winkies
For they're so happy singing their songs.

Sing on! Sing on! Our little bonny babes,
Sing on! Sing on! Our little sugar plum;
We are here listening to your songs.

If only grans could hear them sing,
Only grans could know their words;
Then help their moms to understand.

Their singing means so much to their ears
It will help them through their ensuing years.

COME TO JESUS

Come to Jesus, Come to Jesus now,
He can save us, He can save us now;
When we come to Him, who can come between us?
Love can bind us together, bind us together love.

Let us reach out to Him, reach out to Him now
Ask Him to save us, ask Him to save us now.
He will save us from our sins
If we open up our hearts to Him
An invitation to our hearts is so divine
And that's the way He treasures most.

Ask Him to cleanse our hearts of all evil
Then He'll enter in
He can only do wondrous things
When the heart is pure and free from sin.

Love Him, Love Him, talk to Him, talk to Him,
Reason with Him, tell Him your secrets
The ones that have never been told
He knows them already, but would love
To hear them from your lips
He knows that is true confession
And that's the way to come to Him.

VALENTINE DAY

Alarm bells are ringing on this Valentine Day
Birds are billing and we are cooing,
As Valentine Day is hotting up.

Bulls are running, cocks are crowing,
Donkeys are braying, we are wooing,
Then goes the popping of corks from our bottles.

Kisses and cuddles, embracing and touching
Is what goes on at Valentine's Day.
Let our love shine through on this day,
Let us breathe deep to express our love;
Breathe on me, breathe on me as deep as you can.

Breathe on me, breath of life
Breathe on me, breathe on me
My heart will beat faster when you breathe on me.

Tell all my friends I'm breathing deep
And free as it was meant to be.

LIES

Sometimes I sit and wonder
Why someone has to lie
It is evil it is sheer wickedness,
It can cause the death of a child
And also cause the downfall
Of what was once a wonderful world.

Lies are corruption, lies are painful
Lies are like the scavengers muck
It eats away the very heart of the perpetrator
Heaven forbids the evil character.

Cleanse the heart of muck and hate,
Cleanse the ground on which the footprints tread
And cleanse the grass that grows beneath;
Wash the stones and pebbles on which the footsteps trod.

Heavenly Father hear your cry,
Heavenly Father answer your call,
Falling from your grace and falling in pain
Is this the way the evil one gains
Or is it the way your enemy shines?

YOU ARE

You are the love of our life
You are the good shepherd
You are our guiding star
You inspire us to do justice
You are our redeemer
You are the one who took us from captivity
You show us the way of salvation,
When in distress to You we call
From You our rescue came,
To You we will praise Your name
Through You we will make every effort
To save everything on our planet.

JAMAICA

Jamaicans, Jamaicans from land of my birth,
So wonderfully motivated with voice of our mirth,
Our mountains, our rivers are so highly praised
Our beaches, our huts have human in pairs.
'Oh how wonderful a place we go to explore'
And who will capture the shells on our shore?
Out of one people there are many to say,
This is our patch and we can play.
In Jamaica we can do the rumba,
That beautiful dance we borrowed from Cuba.
Ragga-ragga we can do the reggae
Danced from the top even down to the streggae.

MY MAMA

Delightful, witty, warm and friendly
That's the way my mama was.
She was the kind mama, everyone loved.
I did the things my mama did,
The things she knew were best;
The people loved the things she did
For there was love, faith and respect.

How wonderful a woman my mama was
'As wonderful as the wonders of this world.'
Her graceful charm and magnetic touch
Would reach a heart that has been broken.
Delightful, witty, warm and friendly
That's how my friend describes my mama.
You too can have a mama as dear
To delight us with their witty charm.

BEHOLD

Behold I write, behold I write,
Behold I'll write forever more.
I am a writer and this is what I'm doing,
Behold I write forever more.

BEHOLD I'M LEAVING

Behold I'm leaving my country of birth,
Behold I'm leaving my country of mirth.
Behold my mummy and daddy did cry
When seeing me disappear before their very eyes.

I waved to say bye bye I'm off,
To a country in faraway land,
They gasped with doubt for they won't b e there,
To see me settle to a new life on my own.
'Twas so exciting for me at first,
For I'm now standing on my own two feet
And watching the clock as the hours tick away,
While I'm cooking my first meal in saucepan on my own.
The nights are so long, I lay down crying,
I've missed my parents and that makes me sad.

BRING OUR TROUBLES

Bring us the love we never have,
Bring us the wisdom we adore;
Bring anxiety, bring distress,
Bring our problems to Our Lord.
His presence and endurance
Bring joy to our hearts;
Bring, bring our troubles to the Lord.
Bring the timber, bring the sand
Bring the tools one by one,
With these we will build
That Celestial House,
Where we will bring our prayers to the Lord.
Bring out the bad, bring in the good,
Bring salvation to our land.
Bring back our schools
Bring back our elders.
Bring back the wise,
Bring our troubles to the Lord.
Bring our mothers to our home,
Bring our fathers we adore;
Bring aunts, uncles and cousins
To the school of everlasting peace.
Bring, bring our troubles to the Lord.
Bring us food, bring us water,
Bring us peace, bring us joy,
Bring us the faith we never have
Bring, bring our troubles to the Lord.

SILLY BILLY

Silly Billy, big and sleazy
Robbing the bank with sleazy deals,
If the bank isn't squeezing
Surely Billy will sleaze with ease.

SEARCH

Search for Him, search for Him,
Run to Him, run to Him,
Talk to Him, talk to Him,
Reason with Him, reason with Him,
Plead with Him, plead with Him,
Listen to Him, listen to Him,
'Love Him, love Him, touch Him, touch Him'
He will repair your heart in heaven.
When you open up to Him,
From Him your rescue came
He will never neglect you
For He is God and He will enter in.
'Onward you will walk with Him'
Be a pilgrim with His Christian band,
Tell your love for Him, to everyone
When they see you in Glory shine,
'For your light will be shining bright.'

QUOTATIONS II

1. They who sit and wonder without something special in mind is altogether foolish.

2. Only a fool worries about nothing.

3. The foolish should be helped for they know not what.

4. A fool worries when it rains, then cries when there's no water.

5. A man takes his knowledge to the grave, a woman teaches the entire family with hers.

6. I do not mind dying, the only thing I am worried about is by the following day I will be smelly, stiff and looking up to see how much further I am going in the cloud.

7. Dying is easy, but the pain of dying is awesome.

8. When others close their eyes when they are dying I will open mine just to see who is crying, chatting and looking at my Will.

9. I will not die, I will pass away, I go where there's no night or day.

10. Never leave a bucket around when one is dying in case it is kicked over.

11. I am not worried when I die, I'll only worry how I die and where I die.

12. Common sense is so common, so women have a lot of it. Men do not have it because it is common and nevertheless free. That is why our menfolk are lingering behind.

NO RAIN IN SPAIN

No rain to pour in Spain,
It stopped pouring on the plain
And there's no rain on my windowpane.

For months no rain has fallen,
Each passing day goes by
A hedgehog told me the leaves
Along the hedge are dry,
No water to dampen the leaves,
No dewdrops on the shrubs
Hedgehogs are busy walking
For there's no damp leaves to hide in
And lay their sleepy heads,
They find it hard to fill their days
For there's no place for them to stay.
No rain, parched plain, dry plain, sharp plain,
I'll be catching the early train
For there's no rain pouring in Spain.

A GIRL FROM ANGIPONG

I am a girl from Angipong
I usually have my undies down,
When they are up they are up,
When they are down, they are down,
When the lights went out
I didn't have anything on.

ROLLING UP YONDER

When the rolling ends up yonder,
I'll be there to meet the gander,
With the goose hiding his gender
No wonder he is such a bender.

THE BEAST

'Go' tell the farmers to beware,
The beast of Bolsover will be roaming
On the highlands and their meadow;
'Go' warn the nations that the beast is on its way;
So be prepared for a great escape.

Protect your young ones and your cattle
For the beast will eat them for his supper
'O' roaming beast why art thou so strong?
You that will eat the farmer's flock
Is around us as we watch in fear.

You ate my rabbits from my meadow
And left your footprints in the garden.

IN A BRIXTON

In a Brixton there is no racism,
In a Brixton there is a kind of schism,
In a Brixton the colours are bright,
In a Brixton the people are right,
In a Brixton the people them say
In a Brixton some are gay.
Brixton is the black capital of the world
Where the Rastafarians walk and twirl.
In a Brixton they love the most
In a Brixton they boast the most,
In a Brixton the kids have babes
In a Brixton the goats have kids,
In a Brixton John Major was born
In a Brixton he went to school
In a Brixton he had his first job
In a Brixton he earned his first bob.
In a Brixton they love to say
In a Brixton you have to stay;
In a Brixton they love to play
In a Brixton the police are proud
In a Brixton the cars in pound
In a Brixton the music is loud
In a Brixton the mangoes are sound
In a Brixton David Bowie was born
In a Brixton my son was born,
In a Brixton there is a front line
In a Brixton there is a clothes line.

BUILDING A NEW WORLD

Children of this world answer to the call,
Let your voices be heard and presence seen;
Lift your heads and shout for joy,
We are trying to build a new world
And need your skill, your wisdom
And your charm.

We need to have hope and joy,
See the problems, the fears
The ambitions and the disappointments,
Then we can build an ideal world.

The time, the patience is our pride,
For we are out to solve this problem
And this is a battle we have to win
Time goes on slowly, but time
Can do so much,
Just have patience, we need a bubbling world.

'A world that bubbles with honey and money,'
'A world that bubbles with health and wealth'
And teach mankind to understand
We are building a new world.
'A world that is full of changes'
And must be full of great demands.

We need freedom of expression,
Freedom to demand the things
To make this world a blessed one;
'On our bending knees we will search for liberty,'
And it must come when we have salvation.

It will come without the guns
The bombs and the knives;
'For we are hoping for a peaceful'
And crime free world
as it should always be.

PEANUT THE JACK RUSSELL

'Hi' I am the Jack Russell
From number seven
My name is Peanut and what is yours?
I bark at the cats from my window
And they can tell you how much they fear.
Please postman 'don't knock on my door'
For I'll be sleeping in my master's chair.
The milkman as well is just as rude
For they are always knocking on my door.
I will not hesitate to bite their feet
Although they are so big
I will have a go,
'For I am the Jack Russell from number seven.'
Have you heard of that big black dog next door?
It barks whenever I bark, at anything that passes along
I wonder if he is sane at all.

He acted and continued to act;
Like a cold callous monster for me to dread:
I will tell you my dear
I will not be scared
For I am the Jack Russell from number seven.
I do not eat the things they eat
I eat the things my master eats;
They prepare me nice little chops
Especially the ones from rabbits and lambs.
Sometimes my mum buys me liver and bones
For me to have the strength I need.
I hate the foxes when they're around
For they just keep taking all my bones,
I hate the things they did to me
For they just pee on my mat.

RASCALS

Rascals here, rascals there,
Rascals everywhere.
Rascals to steal the limelight
Rascals on the street
You and I have rascals.
Rascals in the bank,
Rascals in the school,
Rascals in the church,
You and I dislike rascals.
Rascals in the court,
Rascals in the bed,
Rascals in the house,
You and I can be rascals.
Rascals defending you in court,
Rascals defending me in court,
Rascals can be witnesses,
Why should there be rascals?
'Oh rascals, rascals' where are you rascals?

THE ALPHABET

A   is for the alphabet the word
We are trying to establish now

B   is for the Bible the greatest book of all

C   is for Christ the Creator of us all

D   is for December, the month we celebrate our Saviour's
Birthday

E   is for Easter, the time our Lord was crucified

F   is for Father the parent of us all

G   is for grace the thing we would like to be full of

H   is for happy the mood we would like to be in

I   is for intelligence the key to common sense

J   is for January the first month of the year

K   is for Kingdom, the place for the great animals

L   is for liberty the greatest freedom of all

M   is for Mother the carer of us all

N   is for the nobility who pushes us around

O   is for Olive the leaf the dove took home for peace

P   is for the Passover the one Jesus had with his disciples

Q   is for the queen bee the largest bee in the hive

R   is for respect the greatest tribute to all

S   is for Saviour that saves us all

T   is for teacher the one we must respect

U   is for umbrella that shelters us from the rain

V   is for vulgar, keep away from this terrible attitude

W   is for wisdom the one that Solomon asked for

X   has kept us baffled because I cannot express myself

Y   is for year, one hundred makes a century

Z   is for zebra the black and white animal in the jungle
of Africa

Now you see I have established the Alphabet
So learn it with respect.

OUR SPREADING CHESTNUT TREE

Under this spreading chestnut tree
Where we passionately play our games,
How happy we are, under this spreading tree,
Where we spread our love and our glee.
'This chestnut tree, this beautiful tree'
'This spreading tree, this solitary tree'
Has kept us gasping with sheer delight,
Why should it be cut down, in our sight?
Under this spreading chestnut tree,
The police and security guard fought
With protestors screaming, to protect our tree;
Some were saying shame on you, shame on you
We need our tree, our beautiful tree, our spreading tree
'This tree, this tree, this beautiful tree'
The mighty the wonderful the spreading tree,
Why cut it down in the fit of the day
We need our tree our spreading tree;
This tree, this tree our loving tree,
'Our passionate tree, our solitary tree.'

SO MUCH

So much to cry about, there's so much pain,
But I can't cry for there's nothing to gain.
So much to wail about, there's so much weeping
'But I can't wail' for there's no tear
It's all dried up and I am in fear,
Aching me with weakened heart
Trying to put the bad things right
And trying hard to sleep at nights.
How civilised are those that causes pain?
How civilised are those that causes tears?
Their sleazy, slithery motion is always in gear
Goodness knows why they are such a pain,

The uncorrupt is always at their plight
The corrupt is always having a fight
No such Mr Nice Guy anymore,
Politeness, patience and honesty
Is just a word in history.
Ignorance, sleaze and torture
Is now the present word,
One thing we must acknowledge
We are all growing older and should put the bad things right,
'May God' give us grace to behold our mistakes,
To set an example for the 'Human Race'

YOBBOS

How many yobbos at random went,
To destroy a district with violence and hate?
Rioting yobbos with ugly hate and spiteful acts,
Have left the nation reeling in pain and anxiety.
Yobbo, your chants are offensive
Your actions extreme and unforgivable.
Yobbo, lager louts, drug heads
You're causing pain and there's no gain
Oh! Yobbo, yobbo, mindless thugs
Drop your bat and have some fun
'Let's unite, let's go for a run.'
And say farewell to hate and shame
As it should always be.

ANGEL

You are an angel do you know?
You are an angel they told me so,
You sing like an angel,
And dance like an angel,
With angel wings flapping around.
No job too big, no job too small
For you to have no work at all.
I saw you writing on a slab of gold,
With a diamond pen on your fingertips
And words of wisdom from your lips,
I saw you breaking the icy stone.
Your face can look like the Ritz
With coloured patterns from head to toe,
I saw your emotions and saw your joy,
I saw you singing and dancing in glee,
You are the star that shines at night
You are the sunlight that beams at dawn
You are the angel with love so free
I saw you writing in a book of gold,
You're like the diamond that shines on snow
You are the messenger for the love we adore
You are the grace of gracefulness
And will forever be the Angel of our being.

PEOPLE ARE

People are religious and
People are righteous
People are bad and
People are sad
People are fat and
Behave like rats
People are lean and
People are mean
People are singing and
People are dancing
People are aching and
People are searching
People are running and
People are walking
People are talking and
People are waiting
People are people for
People will be people.

PROUD OF YOU

I am proud of you I really am
Your cheeky smile and graceful charm
Will keep me gasping with sheer delight
I fancy having you always in sight.
Heaven knows you are so dear
My mighty you, my wonderful peer
My shining star, with glittering light
Like the one that shines on a snowy night
You are so good, a friend to me
So hold me close for all to see.
My eyes have seen you my gentle one
My ears have heard you singing on and on,
You are here with me, You are here, you are here,
So hold me close my darling dear.
I am so proud of you, I really am
When you play your music as only you can
I dance to the music of our band,
Heaven knows you are so great
Greater than one can understand
That's why I am proud of you
I really am, I really am.

THE SQUIRREL NEXT DOOR

I am the squirrel from next door
That jumps from tree to tree,
I hop the fence and climb the wall,
For you will never see me fall.
The jealous dogs would like me to fall
For they just cannot climb at all.
I will not hesitate to make that leap
Where I'll be safe to have a jump.
I twitch my whiskers and flash my tail,
For you are not there to follow my trail,
I have not been treated with respect?
For I am the one who sew the acorns
From which they have their mighty oak,
That fills their eyes with joy and delight.
The seeds will be buried as I go along,
'For they must be there when I want to eat.'

LOTTERY

The voice to buy lottery tickets
Echoes through the shops,
Just a few more days to go
For this amazing fever.

The nation is ready for some fun,
For lottery fun they will not miss.
Wonderful things we must acknowledge,
That lottery has begun;
Where we gather up the prizes
And buy the things we'd like to share,
Houses, cars, good wine, good food
And handsome gifts to our charming folks.

May the fever of lottery rattle on
For we are happy for the lottery's fun.

FREE IN PARADISE

I heard your welcome voice,
For You alone we cry,
We shall be there with you my Lord
Until our journey's end.

For we are pilgrims, to that onward battle we go,
Fighting for our rights to set us free,
That we can have everlasting peace.

Peace in our hearts, peace in our souls
'Peace be with you my Lord.'

In Babylon, in Babylon where You sat down,
And there You wept, when You remembered Zion
You took us from captivity,
You showed us the way of salvation.

'Oh' let us be free and free to one and all
Through the darkness of the night
We the Pilgrims seek your light
'For You to have us in Your sight.'

MASSACRED

For some schools with classes about
Walls are cracking under awesome cries;
We the teachers are here to defend!
While the children weep and moan.
Seventeen smiling faces were shot and killed,
Twelve smiling faces were wounded and in awesome pain.

Make them painless to earth's madness,
Let us offer prayers of awesome goodness;
'Remember when we went to church,'
We were told we should not kill!
Now, look what he's done to these innocent
Children in our school.

May 'Father' give us grace, to erase this mistake
And have respect for the human race.
Is society to be blamed for this evil to prevail?
'Here we'll unite' as we feel this pain in silence.
Good out of evil must come one day soon,
'For it to remind us' that love must unite us,
Even after death.

A NEW MILLENNIUM

A new millennium beckons
A new era for reforms.
As the twilight begins to fade away
A new dawn has begun,
As the clamour and smoke of this era
Starts smouldering
The battle has just begun to manifest,
A great age for one to compromise
And a great age for the world to change
Leaders of the world should unite
To solve the problems of this beautiful world.
We pollute the air as we fight for breath
Our morals, our freedom, our wealth
And our dignity is almost gone.

MUSIC

I write the music that makes everyone dance;
I write the music which makes everyone laugh;
I write the music, I write the lyrics.

Please dance to my music when listening to my words;
The message I'm saying, I love you so much;
I want you to love me, I want you to hold me.

I write the music, I write the song;
To motivate the old and the young;
Who will find magnetism in their feet.

I write the music that creates harmony;
Homesick 'you will feel' when you hear my song;
It will cling to you, like the wings of a dove.

I write the music for the world to dance;
I write the music and then the whole world laughs.

MUSIC AND DANCE

We shall be dancing at the hall tonight
We shall be dressed in long ball gowns,
Under the chandelier we will rock
And we shall roll to the music of our band.

When the clock strikes one, we'll rock along
To the sound of music in our land
'Rock' to the music, 'Rock'
'Shake' to the music, 'Shake'

In the morning's dimming light,
We've the motivator, day and night;
Life would be an error, without our music
Which appeals to the humble and the noble.

You and I can be prophets of our dance,
When we dance to the music from our band.

SMALL BIRDS SONG

For all the wisdom and power we have,
Earth is dancing when small birds sing;
We, the listeners are here to dance
When small birds are singing their songs.

Perhaps we'll go to the top of the hill,
To hear small birds singing a cheerful song
While earth is dancing to the sound of music
For small birds are singing their songs.

Forward into the meadow we listen with glee,
Downward in the valley some will dance and hum
To the sound of music when small birds sing,
While earth is dancing to their song.

There will always be music in the air,
When small birds are singing a cheerful song,
Sing on, sing on! Small birds, the berries are ripe?
We are here to listen to your songs,
And dance as we go along.

FREE THE SLAVE

I want to break free, I cannot have a vote
And cannot have a say in anything,
To make my life worthwhile,
I have to break free.

I am a slave in a wonderful world,
No one to talk to, not one to listen to,
I have to break free.

I am like a person without a hand
And cannot feed myself,
I am like another without a foot
And cannot stand without a stick,
I have to break free.

I realise I cannot free myself,
The doors are closed, the gates are locked
And the guards are carrying guns,
I have to break free.

'I shouted so loud' the guards were so shocked
They broke the chain that bounded me
'Now' I can proclaim my freedom at last.

BABY DON'T GO

Baby don't go, I don't want you to leave me,
Just hold on baby, 'I am in so much pain'
You see baby, I can't do without you,
Baby don't go, I don't want you to leave me
I'm just waiting, just waiting for you
Baby, baby, baby don't go, please don't go.

I love you, I cry for you, I ache for you
Here I am loving you, 'so please don't go.'
Baby, baby, please don't go, please don't go.

Here I am caressing you, loving you
I hope you realise you are my babe
Baby don't go, I don't want you to leave me.
Just hold on baby, I am in so much pain
Baby, baby, baby please don't go, don't go.

NO

No home, no food, no drink, no wine,
No love, no school, no game, no friend,
No mum, no dad, no sisters, no brothers,
Living in a box on a railway track,
I try to gaze above the passing faces,
And trying to stop my tears from falling.

Help me please, I beg in pain
I'm in despair and there's no gain,
Will society develop a sense of guilt towards my pain?

I am feeling hungry, I'm feeling cold,
My life is ebbing on a railway track,
I've waited long in agony and in pain!
Is anyone there to hear my cry?
'So' I'll sleep and then I'll die.

AWESOME SONG

With all the rings and ropes along,
Earth is echoing into awesome song.
We, the spectators, are to cheer
And the devil will stand and steer.

One may injure, perhaps in the ring so far,
If they are not quick to have their spar,
Onward into the ring they duck and dive
Forward on the rope they lean and strive.

Give one victory to earth's madness,
Let us echo songs of awesome gladness;
Remember when they went to fight,
When they box it has to be right.

Off in danger, off in the ring they roam
Forward on the rope they grunt and groan
One will win, and the other a saddened mess
But he will return, and forget what he missed.
While earth still echoes into awesome song.

I WANT TO BREAK FREE

Follow me, I want to break free
I'm in bondage, I want to break free,
There is a fire burning, I want to break free,
Just follow me, I want to break free.

There is the desert! There's no water
The fire is burning, I want to break free!
Follow me, I want to break free.

Although the journey's so long,
There is no one in sight
To tell of the displeasure I have to endure
Follow me, I want to break free.

When the light stops shining
I'll break the chain that holds my feet
Now I'm free alas, I've broken free.

OH COME

Oh come to the hall in the Wild West
Oh come to the hall with your mate;
No dance is as good as the old reggae
Oh come to the hall and dance.

Dance, dance, dance to the rhythm
Dance, dance, dance to the tune;
No music is as good as the old reggae
Oh come to the hall and dance.

Let your music play, let the body move
This is reggae at its best, make no mistake;
Reggae this is the old reggae
Dance from the top, right down to the streggae.

Welcome to the hall in the Wild West
Welcome to you, and your mate.

SNOWY WEATHER

Slip, slide and slither
Is what we are doing,
On this snowy day.
A nippy day we echo?
I hope you have your woollies on.

My dear aunt, never stood a chance.
She went to feed some birds.
Then she slipped on some snow.
No one was near to hear her cry
And she just froze on the snow.

Avoid going out on a snowy day
For snowy weather we cannot trust.
One minute one is here and the other minute
One may cease to be.

Take care while you slip, slide and slither
In snowy weather,
Just remember my aunt
Who never stood a chance
When she slithered in the snow.

I AM THE POET

I am the poet with poems that hit the market,
I am the poet with verses you want to read.
I am the poet with lyrics so great,
And I wonder why 'I am still in debt.'

I am the poet from down the road,
That writes the lyrics for your song,
I am a poet, make no mistake
This is poetry at its best.

I can write like Shakespeare or Pam Ayres
I am the poet, you should know, for I am late.

Poems are written by fools like me
And only my inspiration can make me write.
I'll write you a poem that makes you feel good
I'll thank you for the praise, while I enjoy the victory.

SUN, EARTH AND WATER

As the dawn breaks and the sun rises,
The earth and its water begins to warm.
Braying asses and birds begin to sing
For a new day has begun?

Upon waters pure and clear
The golden sun is shining on crystal water;
As we water our crops and feed our flocks
We will see some fish in the water perhaps?
Swimming to get the warmth from the golden sun
And aiming to catch the insects that swim along.

As the sun rises at the dawn of day,
We await the time
When midnight darkness shall smite the air
And foxes, owls and badgers hunt for food
Along derelict paths in the forest.

WAR OF SLEAZE

For all the power and wisdom we have
Earth is rocking into malicious word
Let us unite with friendship of old
Let the words echo in the panels of oak.

We may disagree, perhaps in war of words
If we continue our sleaze at work.

Onward into the court we sigh and moan,
Forward into the hall we mope and groan,
Fighting for the love we long to have
While earth is rocking into malicious words.

Let all within us feel the pain,
Of salty sweat that makes us insane,
May we find everlasting peace,
In the place where we sleaze with ease.

I TALK

I talk to the bird
And the bird sings to me
I talk to the tree
And the tree sways to me
I talk to the wind
And the wind blows to me
I talk to the sea
And the sea waves to me
I talk to the dog
And the dog barks to me
I talk to the cat
And the cat miaows to me
I talk to my person
And my person swears at me
Why is my person so rude and crude?
Whilst all the rest did what was best!
Are we the ones with no respect?

OH DIANA

'Oh Diana' I need to dance!
'Oh Diana' I need to dance!
'Oh Diana' I need to dance!
I need to dance, I need to dance.

Send the children out to play!
Send the children out to play!
Send the children out to play!
That we can sing and dance tonight.

'Oh Diana' I need a drink!
'Oh Diana' I need a drink!
'Oh Diana' I need a drink!
I need a drink, I need a drink.

Have a bottle my darling?
Have a bottle my darling, my darling!

AUNT LOUISE

Aunt Louise how are you!
Aunt Louise how are you!
Aunt Louise how are you!
I hope you are well today.

Aunt Louise I want to eat!
Aunt Louise I want to eat!
Aunt Louise I want to eat!
I want to eat, I want to eat.

Aunt Louise I want a drink!
Aunt Louise I want a drink!
Aunt Louise I want a drink!
I want a drink, I want a drink.

Aunt Louise I'm going home!
I'm going home, I'm going home.

WE NEED OUR FREEDOM

Oh this brutal act of slavery
Why keep us in bondage?
When can we have our freedom!

Free us, free us, we need our freedom
We need to see the dawn of day
And the twilight of the evening.

Free us, free us, give us our freedom
Free to go to school and learn,
Free to go to the park and play;
And free to go to church and pray.

Free us, free us, we need our freedom
You took us as captives, you abused us,
You tortured us, you humiliated us
We need our freedom, we need to be free.

Free to have a mind of our own,

Free to have a home of our birth;
Free to have a land of our mirth.

We are growing old and we're growing grey
We need our freedom before the dawn
Of the first day of May.

EXPLORE

As dawn breaks and the sun rises
The earth and its inhabitants begin to explore
The huge forest from which we get our food.

There are so many things to indulge in
There's hardly time to rest and play
Some may catch a pheasant or two
While some may catch a rabbit on the run
There may be some special fruits
'You'll find irresistible not to eat.'
Slip, slide and tumble as you roam the forest,
For this is what to expect when you go along.

'Prickly plants, with awesome prickles'
Sometimes have the prettiest flowers for eyes to see.
Just remember the tasty birds and sweet fruits
You had when you went to the forest,
For they will compensate the hurt you feel,
When roaming the forest in search for food.

'Perhaps' some may not return to the forest
for they were not meant really to explore!
When one reaches the sunset of the day
It will be time to eat, rest and play
Then think of the pleasure of exploring.

A POEM FOR JUSTICE

Look down on us Jesus as we kneel and pray,
Look down on us as we cry in pain,
We are bereaved and there's no gain
'Our Andrew is gone and left many in shame.'
Not only Andrew, there are many more the same.

We are your children and we are in pain
How many are to die, how many are to lie?
How many are wounded and how many are imprisoned?
Where is the justice, where are the judges?
Where is the salvation in this land of ours?

We saw what we saw and what we saw was a dreadful crime.
We saw the murderers captured and saw them set free.
Is this society to be blamed
For this evil to prevail?
We are crying to you Lord to set us free.

Change the heart of hate and spite
Change the heart of rust and stain
And let your Divine love come flowing through
We are your children and we are in pain,
So give us a solution to massage the pain.

GOING HOME

Going home, going home, I am going home
Going home, going home, I am going home
Mama there, papa there
I am going home, going home, going home
I am going home.

Sister there, brother there
I am going home, going home, going home
I am going home.

Grandma there, grandpa there
I am going home, going home, going home
I am going home.

Jesus will be there awaiting my coming
I have reached home! Free at last, free at last!
I have reached home, no more tears, no more pain
I have reached home.

LOVE POTIONS

When we share love portions
Are we in love or just friends?
Is this the beginning or the end
Will we be under the canopy forever?

Let this earth bring forth our increase
With all this energy we have to share
The more I see you, the more I love you
Let our love grow more and more.

When we share love portions
Will it be an apple or a banana?
Darling it will make no difference
For our love is growing stronger and stronger.

The more I think of you the more I love you
For we are bonding, bonding together
Bind us together love, bind us together.

When we share love portions
Will we share our passionate dream?
May my endeavour
Be yours forever?
For I am having a magical dream.

Slumber under the canopy of love
When we share our love portions
We will be together for ever?
'So' hold us together love hold us together
Hold us together in love.

Many hearts have been broken
But ours will go on forever and ever.

FIGHT

We shall fight the battle against aids
We shall fight the battle of common cold,
We shall fight the battle against crime,
On our aching feet we continue to fight.

Fight on, fight on, our mighty comrades,
Fight on fight on our powerful friends
All together we'll fight to win our victory,
The enemies will not prosper,
As long as we have that will to fight.

We shall fight those who rape our siblings,
We shall fight against tyranny,
The tyrants will not prosper
As long as we have that will to fight.

We shall fight against injustice,
We shall fight against racism;
On our aching feet we shall continue to fight.

'Fight on, fight on our mighty comrades'
Fight on, fight on, our powerful friends
All together we will fight to win our victory.

THE GREAT ESCAPE

With all the power and might we have,
Dogs are barking, as burglars pounce,
We the victims are here to lose
Our money, our purses, our everything.

While thieves embark on a getaway train,
Help us please, we beg in pain,
We have lost our living, for the burglars pounce.

Dogs and police searched in vain,
They have caught a train going to sunny Spain
And will never be seen on the plain.

MY HERO

High above shrubs on a twisting road
I saw you dancing on a mountain rock;
It was so spectacular, I had to cry.

Waving in delight, I called my friends,
Just one look at you I yelled!
You are the one that knows no bound.

You're the motivator in this morbid ground,
High above shrubs of twisting road;
I saw you dancing on a mountain rock.

With romantic eyes, I gazed at you and cried,
You are my hero, I want you to know.
Come serenade me with your song.

Gasping in delight I gazed into your eyes
You are my hero, in this morbid ground.

MY PASSING YEARS

I cannot do the same things I did long years ago,
For health and strength have failed me
While nostalgia fills the gap.

The hills and slopes are all as tall
They seem taller than before.
With shaking hands and trembling voice,
I try to sing the songs.

The funniest things about the songs
Is the way the words have changed
I'll hum with grace when the tunes are hard to catch.

How gracious are the years I spent,
How wonderful, are the music and dance.
The beautiful park to go for walks,
With fragrant flowers along the walls.
And floating lilies in the pond
Which helps me to relax as the days go by.

THE SUFFERING OF A NATION

You saw the destruction, you feel the pain,
You saw the people running and crying in vain,
My heart is beating in its cavity
To see the suffering of the human race.

The pain of seeing people begging and weeping,
Is too much to endure, so I'll breathe deep while I can.
The pain, the anger, the homelessness
The supply of food, water and light is gradually fading away.

Oh where! Oh where! Are the morals gone?
Are we cast in the firnament of great fire?
Or is it in the pits of the scavengers' muck?
Where are our leaders gone, the good ones, the uncorrupt?
The one to lead us to the freedom of our birth.

We are looking for a leader to hold our hands,
A leader to be a guiding star.
Far, far away, my eyes are beaming,
On a home that is peaceful and free from war and hate and spite,
Guide us gentle leader, guide us, guide us while we watch in
hope.

Oh where! Oh where! Has our dignity gone?
There is no respect, there is no freedom,
'We have lost it, and we have no hope.'
We need a leader to lead us through
This darkened world, where the sinful and the corrupt will go to
abide;
Then at last we will breathe deep and free,
As God meant it to be.

NURSERY RHYME

Slowly, silently and curiously
We gather up the hedgehogs
Prickles will hurt our fingers
But their fleas cannot bite us.

NURSERY RHYME

You are a nerd
You can't get a bird
For you are observed.

I am not observed
I can get a bird
For I'm not a nerd.

NURSERY RHYME

Bow-wow bow-wow where have you been?
I've been to the master's meadow
To look for his flocks
The night was dark and they were alright
So I left them sleeping and chewing their cuds.

THE FAMILY DEALING

My mummy who sells popcorn,
She is a dealer in the market square
And wherever I go and I hear popcorn
My mummy is there you know.

My daddy who sells old boots,
He is a dealer down the road
And wherever I go and I hear old boots,
My daddy is there you know.

My sister who sells old rings,
She is a dealer in Preston Town
And wherever I go and I hear old rings
My sister is there you know.

My brother who sells fresh fish,
He is a dealer in Brixton Town
And wherever I go and I hear fresh fish
My brother is there you know.

Come all ye family come,
Come to the home and play,
We are together as family again
So let us sing and pray.

BEAUTIFUL

How beautiful are the beauties of this world
Beautiful forest, beautiful people,
Beautiful animals, beautiful insects.
This beautiful planet has surrounded us
With all the beauties of beauty.
Everything is beautiful,
With the exception of sin,
Flowers are the beauties of this world,
How beautiful are the carnations.
Beauty itself is in the eyes of the beholder;
I love beauty, we all love beauty
We are all so beautiful.
All beauties are to be honoured,
Everything is beautiful if it is loved by you.
A beautiful woman is not for flirting
The man who loves her
Will divorce her rather than share her
Beauty can cause so much anger
So much pain, so much strain
Oh beautiful, beautiful people
We are all so beautiful in this beautiful world.

NURSERY RHYME

Merrily! Merrily! Merrily!
Wise men are coming
What a happy time
To celebrate Mary's child.

POEMS

I would like to be a poet
To write poems all day long,
Poems of joy, poems of grief
Poems of laughter and echoing
From this heart of mine.
Poems are written by fools like me
But only God can make me write.
I'll write you a poem
Of that beautiful land where
I'll be writing that La-La Bye
You and me, me and you
Will write together all day long.
Poems are written by fools like me
But only God can make me write.
I'll write you a poem
About the birds and the bees
That will make me so great
Thanks for the priviledge
While I'll enjoy the victory
Poems are written by fools like me
But only God can make me write.

CLIMBING SQUIRREL

Now that summer time is past
And the autumn leaves are falling
All the squirrels are busy hiding
The nuts from the trees in the forest below.
By the way I am Micky the squirrel,
I climb your trees, I pick your nuts
I hid them safe from the birds and rats;
My mother is old and she cannot climb
So I'll take enough for her to eat,
She is so great a Mother to me
So I'll sow the seeds for her to reap,
It is me who sowed the seeds,
From which they have their mighty oak;
I get no respect from the humans at all
For they are so big, they think so little of me.
They know that I am the squirrel
That eats their nuts and climb their trees,
Worry not for me when the winter is here
For I will be asleep in the trunk of the tree.
When the sun comes out I will be there
To gather the nuts I have in mind.
I jump from limb to limb and twig to twig
In the mighty oak tree with spreading branches.
I am so agile to say the least
I kept them wondering how I survive
Remember I am Micky the squirrel
That sow the acorns, climb the trees and eat your nuts.

I AM THE POET

I am the poet with poems that hit the market,
I am the poet with verses you want to read.
I am the poet with lyrics so great,
And I wonder why 'I am still in debt.'

I am the poet from down the road,
That writes the lyrics for your song,
I am a poet, make no mistake
This is poetry at its best.

I can write like Shakespeare or Pam Ayres
I am the poet, you should know, for I am late.

Poems are written by fools like me
And only my inspiration can make me write.
I'll write you a poem that makes you feel good
I'll thank you for the praise, while I enjoy the victory.

A WOMAN IN LOVE

Before I go to sleep
I ask my Lord for my man to keep,
A man to hold, a man to care,
A man to keep me till my days are ended
Oh how can I get a man so dear
When I am so beautiful, to be his Valentine
Alas he came along
With a beam in his eyes
And cheer in his heart
To let me feel where I belong.
Oh how I love this man so dear
To take me in his caring arms
With tears in my eyes and joy in my heart,
I felt my heart beating
With joy and delight,
Oh! Whisper to me my darling dear
Sweet words of comfort, sweet words of cheer
All coming from that heart of yours.
Oh! Let me have your lips my dear,
For you are so desirable, my darling dear
Oh! How I love this man so true,
For us to have an everlasting love
You and me, me and you
Will live together in paradise.
You and me, me and you,
Will share together our body be
Oh! How I love this man so dear
We will share together, till the break of day.
Love is simple to understand
If you've got the one you have in mind
So now you know you've found the one.

SEARCHING

Searching, searching for my father
Along this lonely path
I can only see the blue sky
With no one in sight
There are no birds or animals
That walk this lonesome path
I am sure You are somewhere
For I can see Your footprints in the sand.
I looked east and west
North and south, up and down;
But could not see where
Your footprints start and where it ends.
I know You are somewhere
Maybe too close for me
To see Your face;
But I know You are somewhere
For I can see Your footprints in the sand.
I am still searching for You,
Deep down in my heart
I know You are somewhere near
Nearer than I can ever imagine
You rescued me when I was
Crossing the deserted land
I could not see You
But I could see Your footprint in the sand;
As I walk along that lonely path,
Oh! Breathe on me my loving Father;
For I want to see not only Your footprints
But to know You are here with me until
My journey's end.

CHRISTMAS

Christmas is here, at last the bells are ringing,
The turkeys are roasting, the carols are singing,
The parties are here, and it goes with the rocking and rolling.

In the days of long ago, when men were sad and old,
They loved at Christmas time
To celebrate the birth of their newborn King.

They came from the east, they came from the west,
They came with gifts of frankincense
To celebrate the birth of their newborn King.

They celebrate with legs of lamb,
They celebrate with ox and ham
And dance to the music of the band.
Come on boys and girls, mums and dads,
Uncles and aunts, let's enjoy this Christmas cheer.

The Christmas crackers are cracking,
The mistletoe is breaking as they cuddle below,
The champagne corks are popping
As they celebrate the festive time.

They sang they would rather have Christmas than silver and gold,
When celebrating the birth of our 'Saviour and King.'

POETRY IN ACTION

I'll like to be a poet
To write poems all day long;
About the asses and the cats
And you and I and they and them
Poems are written by sillies like me
'But only my inspiration can make me write.'
I maybe inspired by angels with wings,
Or maybe inspired by wisdom of old;
The inspiration I got is just for you
To find peace, faith and love
In every person you see.
That peace, that faith, that love is so divine
It was only given to one so dear!

This poem I am sending with vision so bright,
For you to view our people in a different light;
That's why I am sending this poem to you
You are like the summer breeze we had
When we're thrashing our rice
And like the one we missed on a hot summer day.

This perhaps is written by sillies like me
And only my inspiration can make me write
For writing poems is my way of expression;
So read it loud for all to hear.
For poems are written by sillies like me
But only my inspiration can make me write.

QUIET

Quiet, listen to your heart beat
Quiet, listen to the sound of music
Quiet, listen to the birds singing
Quiet, listen to the donkeys braying
Quiet, listen to the wind blowing
Quiet, listen to the leaves caressing
Quiet, listen to the church bell ringing
Quiet, listen to the pilgrims coming
Quiet, listen to the Christians talking
Quiet, listen to the members praying
Quiet, listen to the vicar preaching
Quiet, listen to the babies whinging
Quiet, listen to the toddlers trotting
Quiet, listen to the coins dropping
Quiet, listen to the organ sound
Quiet, listen to the choirs singing
Quiet, listen to the footsteps
Quiet, listen to the sipping of wine
Quiet, go placidly to your seat
Quietly kneel and give God thanks
For the bread we ate, the wine we drank
And the reunion we had with Him
Even for just a little while
Quiet, quiet, quiet amid the noise of toddlers trotting.

LOVE DIVINE

Love what a wonderful beautiful love
My darling have for me
The pleasure of this love is so divine
It is so much happier with the passion
We experience, by giving our love to each other.

Love is too pure a light to burn,
The feeling it brings to our embrace.
There are no words that can embrace
The secret of love in our lives!'

'When I say I love you everything is clear'
That means where we go, or what we do.
'Not by demanding but by true understanding'
It only takes you and me to make a love affair.
It is not with blindness that bind us both
'It is by the love we have for each other.'

Love is not dumb, our hearts speak in action
'The language is there, for all to see.'
The roots are deep in this our love
It can stand the wind as fierce as a tornado.

'Love must live and create and be seen'
It is like the old wine that mellows with age,
It causes the heart to beat faster with rhythm
By pumping the blood from head to toe.

SINCE GRAPES

Since grapes are the fruit of love, eat on?
Give me more and more of it
Let me eat of them, for it is love.

Keep mowing, keep mowing, a vineyard, I grow!
To produce the grapes from which wine is made
Let me drink and eat of it, for it is love.

Since grapes are the fruit for none ageing process
Let me eat more and more each day
Fill my bowl with big black grapes!
The blacker they are the more the vitamins
Let me eat more, and more I say.

Eat more and more in your home
Let me eat till the asses are up to bray
And let it be black and safe to eat.

Since grapes are the answer for many a problem
Let me eat more and more each day;
For the benefit of staying young,
And for the love I want to share.

Eat much! Eat much! Much grapes I'll eat!
Let my stomach be filled with many black grapes
Which will help me through my ensuing years.

A CRY IN THE WILDERNESS

Blessed Father look down on us
As we cry for justice
We are crying to the paedophiles
To let our children free to roam.

Our Sarah was tortured, assaulted, then murdered
Not only Sarah!
There are many more the same.
We are your children and we are in pain;

How many are to die, how many are assaulted?
Where is the justice, where are the paedophiles?
Where is the salvation in this country of ours?

Is this society to be blamed
For this evil act to prevail?
We heard what we heard and what we heard was
A dreadful crime.
We are crying to you Father
To set our children free from molesters.

We do not want to be vigilantes,
We do not want to be dictators,
All we want is justice for our babes.

In the wilderness we cry
In our closet we kneel and pray;
'For our children to find freedom to roam,'
we as adults should behave as one
and never use children as our prey.

MY DIAN

Since I met my Dian, my whole life has changed
For a long while I was waiting for this embrace
Now it has arrived, and I am so amused.

'Dian' you are the feathers in my cap
of which I will never let them slip,
'I'll hold on to them even when there's a tornado.'

Oh Dian I love you so much,
Come squeeze me as hard as you can.
I can only feel your heart beat
When you squeeze me, as only you can.

Put your tender lips to mine, then hold me tight,
Breathe on me, breathe on me, as deep as you can.
Dian, Dian I am aching for your love/my Dian!
Dian! You're my babe of that I am sure
So hold me close my darling dear.

Your lips are like the dewdrop on a thirsty plant
Your voice is as eloquent like a robin –
Singing in the highest tree
That's why I waited for you so long.
Breathe on me, breath of life, breathe on me
Breathe on me 'my Dian.'

LOVE EMOTION

Love is the emotion we feel for someone
Sometime from love, joyful tears flow
With inward peace and harmony.

Love is always accompanied
With some element of insanity
And is an experience enjoyed by many.

Love is like war, it always finds a way
To rest in our hearts,
From which the victor hails the flag.

Love is the feeling that grips the heart of people
It wipes away everything
And left one pining for more and more.

When one is in love
There will be no need for inflated emotionalism
Or false piety;
It will be a force of delight to one's endeavour.

Those who experience love
Do not have to search for expression
There will be no need to dredge for act of kindness.

To love somebody is the easiest thing
When you get the one you have in mind
One's heart will beat faster,
One's heart will beat louder;
And one's heart will be pumping blood all over
True emotional feelings has begun
And will embrace your love with sheer delight.

SORROW AND WISDOM

From just a little wisdom
Mighty sorrow display.
On bending knees I prayed to God
To release me from snares and torture.

From just a little wisdom I echoed,
Grey power is on the march;
I am growing older so wisdom is thriving
And it comes with mighty sorrow.

Some of the effects of this are welcome
For now I can see who my true friends are
We may become a more decent cultured citizen
When we realise that some of us are more gifted
And to inflict hostility is not the answer.

To grow old with wisdom
Is to pass from anger to compassion
From anxiety to peace
And from sorrow to happiness.

In personal terms I echoed,
This is a gift of life to treasure
And only with wisdom for a good measure.

SUNRISE

The night is wet, with a light glow,
There awaits the risen sunlight that hangs between;
The surface of the evening cloud below.

Sunrise that came with ripen fruitfulness
Then came the sweetness from the burning sun;
Consuming the love with amazing greatfulness.

Along the street the dawn awaken,
With cloudy dewdrops on the leaves;
Which water the roots that farmers forsaken.

Wives in bright red and green frocks
Watch in glee at their ripened fruits
And admiring their husband with their flocks.

The berries ripened in the burning sun
With sweetest fruits for little birds fun.

QUOTATIONS III

1   If a parent or guardian train a child in the right way that child when old will not forget it.

2   Look at the Cathedrals, admire the trees, breathe on the roses all what you have seen are beautiful.

3   A person who sends others to war, never allow their sons or their family to fight in the battle front. Their lives are precious, but others are not.

4   He who hates me will hate my mother, for she's the one who taught me.

5   Whatever happens in a decade, another ten years will destroy.

6   War is evil, no matter how near or far, it corrupts even the pure in heart.

7   War is like the disease of the brain, where some are obsessed with evil.

8   Never marry a person for their good looks, there are many more important things to take in consideration.

9   If a man does not love his mother, how can he love his wife, never mind his concubine?

10   Never count on your crop, before it is harvested.

11   Never marry a masculine man for his fertility.

12   A working person values time, to a lazy person time is not a problem, because they never find it necessary to work or play.

13   Ask not what your parents have done for you, say what you have done for them. First they gave us life, so you can imagine the rest that comes after.

14   Liars are always telling people not to trust others, but to put their trust in them

PEANUT THE JACK RUSSELL

There lived in a house in the secluded part of Greenwich a man, his wife and four children. They had four dogs who were Jack Russells and I was one of them. The name of my mother was Suzy and my father's name was Rover.

My master said I was the most intelligent dog he had ever seen. Because I was so intelligent I became the favourite of the family. They would give me all the love they could, followed by all the nice bits they could afford. All the other dogs in the area became jealous of me.

One day my master planned to take a holiday with his wife, and decided to take their four children and us the Jack Russells to their parents for them to take care of us until they returned. I was not too pleased about this, therefore, out of sheer frustration I started to fight my brother, whose name was Jasper. 'Oh, don't do that,' said my master's parents 'you must not fight.' They muttered. 'I will continue to fight' said I to my new master. I snarled at them, then I barked for them to see how angry I was. Luckily my old master was not gone as yet. They rang a friend they had and told them of their fear for us. Their parents were elderly and therefore, would not be able to take care of us and put up with my behaviour. His friend told him that he was able to provide a home for me. I was glad because I would have all the attention I wanted with this big family. I was to be the only dog in the family.

My new master and his wife came to pick me up and that was to become the end of my first family relationship. As soon as they entered the door I wagged my tail and had a good sniff. They seemed very good I muttered. I was so excited. I started to run around the room uncontrollably. My mother and brothers were very sad by the thought of losing me. I assured her that I will visit her until my new master was ready. The sad thing was to say goodbye to my mother, although I feared one day that something like this could happen. Now my next fear was to be accepted by my new master's children. I started on this long journey by car to my new home.

When they reached home, to my surprise, I was taken up in my master's arm. This was really a good beginning. He opened the door and his four children came to greet me. This was really the attention I needed to love and be loved. The atmosphere seemed very good for a Jack Russell like me. I sniffed everyone individually before I chose my favourite. My new mistress was the heart of my life. She would cook for me nice chops, especially rabbits and lamb. One day my master's friend came to visit the family and as he knocked on the door I started to bark because I thought he was an intruder. 'Go away!' he said, you are no bigger than a peanut. How on earth could be know that my name is Peanut? It was a mystery. One thing he did not know was that I am a Jack Russell. He became one of my best friends over the years.

One day I decided to go down the road by myself. My master did not know where I was and began to look for me. As I heard him calling me I ran through the fence and entered the house through the back door. They wondered if I was sick as I did not bark at the Postman. The reason for my disquiet was my guilty conscience. I knew I had done wrong in straying from my master. After all I should have known better because I was brought up in a busy area of London. I was such an unusual dog I would show my skills to all the other dogs in the area. Everyone in the district knew me. Not because of my friendliness but because of my cute appearance and my independence. I knew I was cute because my owners told me so. My brown and white colours made me entirely different from all the other Jack Russells in the community.

One day as I was running in the forest and a few yards in front of me were some squirrels and foxes. I decided to chase them around the bend. They were not expecting any trouble from me because they had heard how friendly and considerate a Jack Russell I was. I said to them, 'If you want to continue living you will have to get away as fast as you can.' I snarled and barked as loud as I could. 'One word from you and you will have my teeth ripping you apart. 'I do not like foxes any more!' I said 'because you stole my bones and worse of all you wee on my mat. This is humiliating to a Jack Russell like me. There was such a desperate

167

look in the foxes face that the squirrel lay still her heart thumping painfully with fear of my ferocious teeth. The squirrels made a run for it straight up the trees. They jumped from limb to limb and from branch to branch just to get away from me. The agility in their movements was so spectacular that I stood there looking in amazement. The squirrels heard the foxes terrified voices promising obedience to me. The foxes vowed not to take my bones nor pee on my mat anymore. For a while there was complete silence from the fox, the squirrel and me. Then we all went our separate way. When I got home my master asked me where I was. I replied angrily 'What has my absence got to do with you?' My master said to me that I should be in the house to protect it from intruders. I told my master what the foxes had done to me. My master laughed when I told him of the disgusting things the foxes had done to me. I said 'Well as from now on I will remain in the house and will not chase the foxes when they start peeing on your vegetables and poo on your lawn. 'Foxes are not nice animals,' I said to my master. 'They can be very evil and they also steal.'

One August morning my master and I went for a walk in the park, where we met his friend Bob and his dog. Bob's dog is a Great Dane. 'Good morning,' said my master to Bob the master of the Great Dane. 'What a beautiful dog you have got,' said my master. 'His name is Hector,' replied Bob. 'The name of my Jack Russell is Peanut' said my master. 'What a beautiful coat your Jack Russell's got. Hector was jealous of me because everyone in the park was looking at me with admiration.

Men, women, dogs, foxes and squirrels were wooing me. I started to hop around the park on three legs and did the most amazing thing they could ever behold. I did not love Bob, Hector's master, so I did the same thing the foxes did to me. I peed on his foot for Hector to have my scent when he got home. My master was not happy nor surprised with what I had done, because he knew that I am, who I am, the Jack Russell from number seven. 'Wait' I said 'Have you heard of that big black dog from number nine who barks whenever I bark? He acted and continues to act like a cold callous monster for me to dread. Sometimes I wonder if he is sane at all. He pretends to be ferocious just to make me scared. He is forgetting one thing that I am the Jack Russell from next door. I was so respected by my master that he would take me wherever they are going. He was not privileged to get this treatment, because he was not witty as my master and that was one of the reasons for my mannerism.'

As time went by the family of six started to move home one by one. I became less and less active but more and more intelligent. These things do not seem to come hand in hand. Years started to show on my whiskers, because they started to become grey. Sometimes I wish other dogs could be like me. I played upon my master's kindness, but then again if I was not clever and intelligent my master would not be caring as he is. He was loved by everyone who knew me. I would bring laughter to their faces. Nothing can be more comforting than a good laugh from your master, and I was good in supplying this. If my master is sad, I am sad, if he sings, I sing. As I go through life I try and do as many things my master did to gain the things I wanted in life. I noticed how life is hard for the squirrels when they have to separate the nuts from the shell.

The cats and foxes are always running around and trying to catch the rats and await the opportunity to steal my bone. Look I said to my master, those poor animals can hardly survive if only they have nice people to teach them the way of survival. They too could be like me, if only they could adjust to your style. 'We can try to get closer to them,' said Peanut. 'Yes' said I. If we put some nuts and some pieces of meat outside the door they would come and have it I promise said I to my master. I will not bark nor snarl at them. 'That would frighten them away' said my master. We will put more and more each day, so that they will become dependent on us. 'Yes' said my master to me. I must wag my tail and let them see that I am friendly and caring.

One day my master went out and the fox came to the door of my house. The only thing that separated us was the thickness of the glass. We just stood there gazing into one another's eyes. It was quite an experience because it had not happened before. I was glad to have gained the foxes confidence. As time went by the foxes would take their cubs to see me. We became the best of friends.

They stopped taking my bones and peeing on my mat. One confidence left for me to gain was that of the squirrels. The process was slow, but I knew in my heart that I would succeed. After a week of slow progress I could see that the squirrel was becoming friendly, and all the dogs in the forest hate me because I was friendly with the foxes, the squirrels and the cats.

THE MASSACRE

How could they do that to innocent children and people? Try as we may, we cannot escape the fact that over recent years the news has not simply been bad, it has become almost unbelievable. As soon as one enters out one will hear people saying 'What are we coming to?' 'How much more of these awful illnesses can we take?' 'Where on earth have these murderers come from?' 'It is going from bad to worse from one country to another.' 'Where oh where have morals gone?' There is not much we can do to stop it. The most recent of these are the children in Dumblane and many other countries throughout the world.

We saw the destruction, we feel the pain, we saw people running and crying in pain. The suffering of the human race is so intense, therefore for those who the villains have not yet reached have got to breathe deep while they can. The evil of today has visited our home, our school, our street, and even our shops. There are so many questions with only a few answers. Are the bureaucrats to be blamed or is it our society? Something is wrong somewhere, of that I am absolutely sure. They make our society what it is, choices for good or ill, but there is hardly any good, all we are beholding is evil. Honesty in all things and at every level is a protest against so many things which seem hopeless and second rate. It produces a society which is prepared to accept less than the best.

Let us start from the grass root, our churches, some are not doing well, for so often one will read about the vicar having an affair with a parishioner's wife, or molesting our little children. If it is in that, which we ought to have faith, has let us down, then what more can we confide in? In places like the House of Commons some of our ministers are having affairs and in the home one is witnessing one of their parents having an affair. Now let's face it! We have broken down the very fabric of our society. We are rotten to the very core. Famous stars must set an example for our children they are always modelling themselves after famous people, for they too would like to be as famous as their hero. The problem of our young people going astray often conceals the failure of the older generation to take responsibility and show guidance to our young people. A defiant behaviour is natural among young men especially the difference between the young people of today and the young of times gone by is not that different only that some are caught up in a hopeless zone. We must express our feelings and let good come out of evil, remember evil cannot overcome good. If we all should endeavour to maintain the power of good, evil will be eradicated from our hearts. Evil only enters the heart when it is empty of positive belief. Evil is always awaiting someone who is vacant and is ready to accept their command. Children should be taught right from wrong at an early stage of their lives, long before going to nursery school. Parents should have at least two children, for with two or more they can communicate and nevertheless thrash out their differences. These differences can be so trivial, but then they have mums and dads guidance. These differences can be so trivial but that's where evil can begin if not rooted out. Give our children hope, give our children freedom and set our children free. They will be the people of tomorrow and we are the people of today, let us join hands and hearts together and give our children a decent world. Change the evil of society and make it a crime free one. We are intelligent therefore we should use that intelligence to create a decent world not only for our people but for everyone that lives in it.

We can create massacre not only on one another, but on animals, insects, birds and plants, all are important for our being. We must realise that we are humans and are the most intelligent of these creatures. Perhaps we should take a grim look at how we treat others, who may be of a different gender, colour or country. Look how the rich treat the poor? Are we not wise to see what we are doing is wrong? When will we learn that we should give to others who are less fortunate. God made one world for the people and one market for trading our goods, so why can we not do likewise. Sisters and brothers must unite for the causes of the human race, that by protecting ourselves from pollution and others from massacre.

We got to make sure of yesterday, for there may be no tomorrow if we continue to massacre our people and other things. In my heart and I know there are some good people out there that will bring us new hope and will bring us awesome gladness. May we look beyond this awful word 'massacre' and find the joy of goodness in our hearts, may goodness and gladness be the motto for the coming years.

HELP

Once, there lived in the country of Zing, a sow, a boar, some piglets and a bulldog. They decided to set up home in this remote part, because they needed complete privacy. Food was very scarce because the country was suffering from drought.

The piglets were very fond of their mother for her loving kindness towards them, so they wanted to show her all the respect they could. Instead of calling her sow or mother they called her Sour as a pet name. As time went by they wanted to ask her about her mouth, not knowing that it would offend her. They said 'Sour, we wanted to ask you for some time why your mouth is pointed, we mean long really?' said the piglet. 'Look' said the sow to the piglets, 'When you have a father like yours and piglets like you all, what do you expect my mouth to look like? It is still shorter than that of a coyote. You are all growing up and one day your mouth may be longer than mine. With things as difficult as they are now, there will be no stopping to this hardship. Life is getting harder and harder' she muttered.

'Look' said the sow, 'When I was expecting you my mouth was as short as that of the bulldog and look what I am looking like now? Your daddy is always telling me to have some more piglets, while you are all demanding nearly all of my food.'

The piglets took one look at their dad and said 'Can't you just leave Mum alone so that her mouth can become shorter.' Dad was very quiet. The reason for this was because their mum had told the piglets that he was constantly asking her to have some more piglets. 'No, no, I will not have any more piglets,' she said to them, 'I Have got more than enough on my hands. No way,' she muttered, 'you can adopt some if you want to and take care of them yourself,' she said to the boar. 'OK I will' said the boar. Away he went and asked a sow in another district if she would let him take care of her piglets. 'Oh how nice of you' she said to the boar. 'You can have all of my piglets, no problem at all.' The boar took only two of her piglets home because she was too willing to let him have them. One thing, he had to get in the habit of taking care of these greedy piglets. Within four weeks of caring for these piglets, his mouth was longer than that of his

174

mate, Sour. She looked at him and said, 'Now you tell your children how easy it is for a pretty short mouth pig to have a mouth looking like that of a coyote.' 'It's not fair,' he said. 'I did not know that mothers could have things so hard. We will have to look at your life differently from now on. Just look at what has become of my mouth in one month!' 'Then what will it look like in two or more months and what other damage can be done to you my dear?'

'I will have to tell all of the males in the area what I have experienced. They will look at the plight of the female in a different light. Ump ump' he said and away he went, and told the males in the neighbouring area how to treat the females with piglets with a lot more respect. He said 'Look what I have experienced in one month. I honestly do not know how the females really put up with their horrible task. There am I asking her to have more piglets and all her piglets demanding her food, and sucking the life out of her. Ump ump, we have got to change our attitude,' he said.

All of the males promised to help in every possible way they could to make life easier for the females. So you see, if the boar did not have this terrible experience, he would not have known that the females had such a hard task to fulfil, such as to be a mate, a mother and a friend.

FOXES AND BIRDS PARTY

A very long time ago, there lived in the forest of Keston Park, some animals and birds.

One day, all of these creatures decided to have a party to prove to the other creatures in Farnborough park that they could be friends although they were of a different nature. The foxes, hedgehogs, cats, badgers and squirrels went to the birds and arranged the date for this party and told them that they should let the insects know the time they decided to have this party. The insects would be their guests of honour. The kind of birds that there were, were owls, robins, sparrows, blackbirds, ducks and pigeons.

The leader of the animals were the foxes. They were selected because they were always so smart. 'Well' said the smartest fox of the pack, 'I will have to make all the plans.' The birds chose the most clever of the lot which is the robin. These two got together and arranged this wonderful party. It was to take place at the Keston Lake's Common. They caught frogs, toads, spiders, rats, mice and earthworms for this wonderful feast.

When all the animals, birds and insects arrived for this party, it was not really a happy occasion because the insects did not like what they saw as their tastiest morsel. The insects decided to go home as soon as they saw what was on the menu for their meals. 'Where are you going?' said the animals and the birds. 'Home' said the insects. 'We do not really love your company, not when you have those morsels for your meal. Surely you could have prepared something else.' 'Look, it's not any of your friends,' said the fox and the robin, 'They are from another area.' 'We still want to go if that's what you think of us,' said the insects, and away they went.

The party was left with the animals and the birds They ate and they ate. When they had finished eating they decided to have some music so that they could dance. As soon as they decided to have some music, they decided to have a rest, and to think up a new trap for those poor insects. The things they had in mind was to capture these poor insects to have a variety of tasty morsels. 'Insects are not really stupid you know' said the birds, 'Just because they saw those prepared on the lawn, they said they were not interested in our party,' the birds said to one another. 'The same way we tried to capture those innocent insects at our party, it is the same way those humans in the park could trap us.'

'We have got to be careful,' said the birds. 'The same goes for us' said the witty fox to the others. 'They will use us for their coating. I saw a human with some foxes coating on her body. Deep down I think they will want to trap us for our coat' said one fox to the other animals. They said to the hedgehog. 'You are very lucky to have prickles on your body and a lot of fleas. Humans do not like that' said the foxes and badgers. 'As for us, we hardly stand a chance.' 'Speak for yourselves' said the badgers. 'I'll hide away in the daytime and seek my food at nights' said one fox to the other. 'I will promise you they will never have my coat and, furthermore, we will prove to them that we are clever animals from Keston Park who will never give into human tricks!'

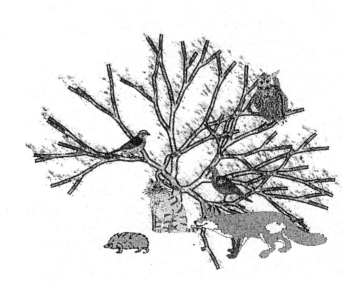

THE RABBIT, THE BIRD AND THE HEDGEHOG

Once there lived in a meadow called Oz, a rabbit, a bird and a hedgehog.

One day the rabbit said to the bird and the hedgehog that they should go to the island called 'Apples' where they could have all kinds of delicious fruits to eat.

The rabbit could not fly so he asked the bird to lend him some of his feathers to enable him to fly. The hedgehog could not fly as well, therefore he asked the bird to lend him some of his feathers so that they could all go together to this beautiful island.

The bird decided to lend them the feathers, so that they could all go at the same time. They said they would go as soon as the rainy season was over. Alas it stopped raining. Therefore they got the feathers from the bird. As soon as they got it, they glued it on their bodies and away they flew to the island called 'Apples'.

When they reached there, they could not believe the things they saw because the place was so beautiful with all those delicious fruits. Now the hedgehog was so grateful to the bird for lending him some of his feathers, that he decided to call him brother bird. The rabbit was very ungrateful so he decided not to talk nor laugh with the bird nor the hedgehog. He thinks that because he is now on this beautiful island he would not need the bird nor the hedgehog anymore.

He called the bird and said 'You stupid little creature you can have back your awful feathers, I do not need them anymore.' 'What!' said the bird 'you do not need my feathers?' 'Yes' said the rabbit 'I do not need your feathers nor your company.' 'Right' said the bird 'I will have my feathers back' he said. 'Then' said the rabbit to the hedgehog, 'I do not need your company as well.'

The hedgehog went and told the bird what this awful rabbit said, the two of them decided to be the best of friends, and one day soon they will leave the island of 'Apples'.

As the cold season drew near the bird gave the hedgehog some extra feathers so that he could have an easy flight. They flew back to the meadow of 'Oz' and left the awful rabbit behind. Little did the rabbit know that when the cold spell started there would not be any more delicious fruits in that beautiful island, plus he would be left with all strangers like the wolf, the fox and the eagle.

Now that the fruits had disappeared the rabbit had the honour of being the centre of attraction on the island. The eagle, the fox and the wolf all got together, took one look at the rabbit and said that one is mine. I wonder what happened to the rabbit?

IN THE COUNTRY OF PING

There lived in the country of Ping a man, his wife and two children. They had two dogs, two cats and two rabbits. One day the man whose name is Alfie said to his wife whose name is Maise that they should build a cage, so that they could purchase some exotic birds to live in it.

The names of their children are Charlie and Annie. Alfie said 'Maise let us go down the road to Tom's shop and buy a pair of parrots, which I'm sure our children will be proud to have. The parrots we will pick must be the most amusing ones in the shop.' They paid Tom the amount of money he wanted for the parrots. 'Look' said Tom to Alfie and Maise, 'You can buy your parrots food from me because my parrots food is always the best in the area.' 'OK' said Alfie 'Let me have a bag or two.' 'Yes' said Tom, 'and do come back when it is finished.' When they took the pair of parrots home, Charlie and Annie were very excited to have such a pair of exotic birds. 'Let's name them Pat and Liz' said Charlie. 'The names are pretty' said Annie. These parrots can already say a few works like 'Pretty Polly'. Charlie and Annie promised they would make it their duty to teach the birds to talk properly. Pat and Liz were very willing to learn, that within a couple of months they knew at least thirty words. They could even sing some nursery rhymes, but preferred it being called 'Parrots Rhyme'.

These parrots were so amazing that whenever the family are going out they would let Liz and Pat out of their cages to roam around the house and to protect their possessions from thieves. Pat was very vicious and mischievous when approached by a stranger. No one could dare enter through the door without Pat being told they are friends, for he would surely attack them. The dogs and cats became so jealous of the parrots because their owners had paid too much attention to them. Pat the aggressor would call the dogs snarling dogs. This causes the dogs so much stress that they threatened to bite them whenever they were out of their cage. 'They will make that mistake and sit on the settee or the chair' said the dogs to the cats.

Pat and Liz heard and therefore called the dogs, snarling dogs, but did not call the cats any names, because they knew the cats could be a threat to them. 'Cats can climb' said Pat to Liz 'so we've got to be careful.' 'I will have that parrot and the other one' the dog muttered. 'Soon all the dogs in the area will be jealous of me having parrots for my meal.' 'One parrot, two parrots' the snarling dogs muttered! Na-Na - Na-Na fancy having – in par- rot for dinner, er?.

The parrots heard and asked Alfie, Maise, Charlie and Annie to show more attention to the dogs and cats for their own safety. 'Look' said Pat 'They are serious. Please be kind to them, for they are threatening to eat us.' 'We can't have that.' Said Alfie. 'Look' he said to Maise, 'The parrots told me they are scared for their lives, for the dogs and the cats threatened to eat them. They went as far as to make a song of it.' 'What!' said Maise 'We have to pay more attention to them and with a lot of respect.' 'We love them all don't we? Therefore it would be heartbreaking to know that the dogs as well as the cats are not happy and rightly so too. We have really forgotten those poor animals. But how did this really happen? One thing we have forgotten is that dogs as well as cats are extremely intelligent and should be treated accordingly. It is strange to see how they bottled up this anger for so long. No wonder sometimes when I called them they pretended not to hear. Now I know why and I promise you this will never happen again.'

Maise called Charlie and Annie and told them what the dogs and the cats were threatening to do to Pat and Liz. 'Oh! Mum' said Charlie. 'I have noticed this for a long time, but failed to know what was the cause. To be honest sometimes I thought it was the food, that different brand we bought down the side walk market. Then again sometimes I thought it was the rain and above all the cold spell. How foolish we were to ignore those signs. Well' said Charlie, 'I'll put my hands on my heart and promise you Mum that I will treat them equally. First and foremost as day breaks I will be going down Tom's shop to buy some special food and treats for them. Secondly I will endeavour to take them to the meadow where they will chase the squirrels and other furry animals.' Pat and Liz were very happy when they heard everyone vowing to treat the dogs and cats with respect. 'Look' said Pat to Liz, 'we too can do our share to be equally friendly to those snarly dogs and miserly cats.' 'Can't they not give that little honour to those animals?' said Annie. Although they promised to be friendly? 'I hope they have not heard them' said Charlie to Annie. 'No' said Pat to Liz, 'Did we say it loud?' 'No we don't thank parrot goodness., it was not loud. Let us sing to them some parrot rhyme and do some press ups as well. These will let them feel good, really good,' said Pat to Liz. 'Let us sing them this rhyme, the words are 'You are a nerd. You can't get a bird, for you are observed. I am not a nerd, I can get a bird, for I am not observed.' Said the dogs to the cats, 'We should have known better from the start, for look that Alfie, that Maise, that Charlie and Annie did not even have that respect to give us a name. They simply called us dogs and cats. No wonder red beak, smelly breath, dry feet bud does not have any respect for us.'

'Now, that everyone is giving us respect,' said the dogs to the cats, 'it doesn't mean we should let our bond of affection fade.' I wonder what language is understood between a parrot, a dog, a cat and a person.

THE TORTOISE, THE SNAIL AND THE ELEPHANT

The tortoise started to laugh when he was told that the elephant was going to have a baby calf. 'Oh, plup! Plup! Plup!' said the tortoise. 'How interesting I will go and call the midwife for you if you ask me to.' 'Why not?' said the elephant!

The tortoise started on this journey as soon as he was told by the elephant. He was given twenty months in advance to travel the two miles journey to reach the midwife. The baby calf was born before the tortoise reached the end of the journey. The snail said to the tortoise that he could reach there much quicker. 'Oh plup! Plup! Plup!' said the tortoise. Man you do not know how fast I ran.' Sometimes there was heavy rain, then came the shining sun which made the journey on the road very slippery. 'Man I worked hard, very hard, to reach this midwife. Let's face it, I was just a little bit late. Next time I hope she will tell me before she decides to have another calf, to go and call the midwife. This time I will be there in a flash. I will not let my friend the snail laugh at me.'

The snail said to the tortoise, that the next time he is called to do this kind of errand he's got to be quick. How humiliating' said the tortoise. 'Oh, plup! Plup! Plup! Well if that is the way you are undermining my effort, I will never try again. Humiliation is a thing I cannot accept.' 'Yes' said the snail. 'I can see how upset you are. You know something' said the snail, 'sometimes when I am on my mission, some human would put salt in my path or even slug pellets. Now that is not even humiliation, that is just simply death.' 'Oh plup! Plup!, Said the tortoise, 'mine is much better.'

BEG, STEAL OR BORROW
THE DOG, THE CAT AND THE RAT

'I will beg' said the dog, 'by putting my paws up for someone to have pity on me.' 'I will borrow,' said the cat, 'by rolling over and over and making miaow, miaow sounds.' 'I will hide away,' said the rat, 'then whenever no one is around, I will simply steal to fill my belly.' 'How dis-gust-ing' said the dog and the cat to the rat. 'You must learn to have respect for yourself.'

'Trying to steal from humans in their absence is really a bad thing. I do not want to humble myself' said the rat. 'I prefer to be a thief.' 'No' said the dog, 'that is where you are totally wrong.. 'Ah!' said the cat, now I know why your name is a rat, because you are always a thief and a horrible one.' Said the dog to the cat and rat, 'I am always my master's best friend because I can do so many things for them, and other friends.' The cat said, 'the same goes to me, I can do a lot for my master and the community. You see that enemy over there? We will be forever killing it, because it is always stealing and leaving droppings in my master's cupboard.'

'How dis-gus-ting you are,' said the cat. 'No wonder I am always watching out for you, when you enter my master's home. I know some cats and dogs do steal sometimes, but it is not a habit, for we are always working for our keep.' Said the rat to the cat and dog, 'Do you know some humans steal as well. That's why when they steal, others who do not will call them a rat. The name rat is not a nice word to be called.'

The rat said to the cat and dog,' that it can sleep all day and night if necessary, as long as there are footsteps around, I will hide away. I can never tell you that I have any other friends apart from rodents, like myself.'

'That's a lonely life' said the cat to the dog and rat. 'We are never lonely, we are always busy making so m any friends.' 'Whenever they are around. I do not like humans and cats especially, ' said the rat. 'With dogs it is not as bad, I can just about make rings around them. I love to tease them by just hiding in a little corner where they can't catch me. They will sniff and bark but they just can't catch me,' said the rat to the cat and dog.

'Be very careful of what you are saying because I am my master's best friend and they are willing to help me to catch you if I ask them to.'

'Watch your space,' said the cat, 'for I would love to be in that chase, because you seem very sure about yourself. You are a rat and no one will have any love for you. You caused the great plague of Britain where so many people died, so be very, very careful. We sometimes borrow from our masters and repay them with our service. Because we are willing we do as we are told, they would even take us on holidays with them and that cannot be bad. Life is always an adventure to us, for we do not need to steal and hide.

IN A COUNTRY CALLED TUDD

There once lived in a country called Tudd, a man by the name of Ozzie, his wife Maria and their four children. One bright sunny day, Ozzie said to Maria that they should get two cows and some pigs to live on their farm. Maria was very happy by this idea, so she went and told the children this happy news. One of the cows names will be Molly and the other Cuddy. The children thought it was very funny to call one of the cows Cuddy.

'This Cuddy is always chewing her cud' said Ozzie, to make sure she can digest her food when she is having a rest. 'Why do they just keep chewing so often?' said the smallest child, who's name is Audley. 'They just like to chew their cud' said Ozzie. 'I like Cuddy more than Molly,' the eldest child muttered! She is always looking around as if to say who we are? You can tell she is very clever and wants to make us happy when we are around her paddock. She would say moo, moo then she would start walking around in circles as if she is having a dance. She would do things like some of the animals we saw at the circus. 'Molly is not as nice' said Ozzie, 'but she is the one that gives Cuddy the assurance to carry on entertaining us. Cuddy and Molly will one day have calves, then we will have much more fun,' said Maria.

'Birds are always hanging around these cows,' said Tim the eldest child to his father Ozzie. 'Don't you know why?' said Ozzie. 'Because cows usually have ticks and lice, therefore they would follow the cows around to pick off the parasites. The cows love birds for this. They usually become friends after a while.' The birds would sing melodious songs for Molly and Cuddy.

'No wonder' said Tim, 'they are so happy. Now I know why, they in return would say moo, moo and walk around in circles as if they were per-for-ming in the circus.' Tim said to his dad that sometimes he saw some birds doing press ups as if they are entertaining the cows. 'How amazing?' said Ozzie. 'Not only do they sing for the cows, do press ups, they also pick the fleas, tics and flies off them.'

'Now I know! Now I know!' said Tim. 'Birds and cows will always be friends because they care for each other in their own little way. They are even keeping each other company, providing food and relieving them from the parasites. We too are their friends because we prepare the paddock for them, so you see we all depend on each other for our being.'

PLAY – SADIE AND DENSIL

Sadie	'Hello darling, how are you?'
Densil	'I am fine dear, where are you calling from?'
Sadie	'What do you mean where am I calling from, when I have already told you I was going to Jamaica.'
Densil	'I did not mean it in that way. I meant to say if you were at your parents home or in a hotel?'
Sadie	'I could not afford to stay in a hotel when my parents home is just around the corner, plus I can have all the privileges I desire.'
Densil	'I am ready to come down there darling, I can't stand being away from you darling.'
Sadie	'Oh how sweet of you. I will be looking forward to have you as early as possible.'
Densil	I'll see you in the morning darling? I'll be coming on Concorde.'
Sadie	'You may not see me in the morning darling, because I will be going to Manchester for a modelling job in the nearby store.'
Densil	'You mean I cannot see you immediately as I reach Jamaica? But the journey from the airport to where you are, is only thirty minutes drive away.'
Sadie	'Just call me if you reach before 8am. I will send a cab to pick you up.'
Densil	'Ah how wonderful. You are really so sweet.'
Sadie	'I saw Crissie yesterday and I told her you will be coming tomorrow. She was very excited and will be looking forward to see you.'

Densil	'We will all have a merry time together, especially going to the seaside.'
Sadie	'Good morning Crissie, how are you? Densil will be here tomorrow as planned.'
Crissie	'Oh how wonderful. Oh how sweet. He is such a nice guy, your parents and family should be proud to have such a wonderful young man as Densil.'

The cab driver said to him, 'Are you Sadie's friend?'

Densil	'Yes.' This is really a wonderful, beautiful place. I can't wait to see my darling Sadie.'
Cabbie	'She is such a beautiful lady. You must be lucky to have her.'
Densil	'Lucky, you,' he said? 'She is lucky to have me too. Yes, we are both lucky to have each other.'

Sadie said to Densil as soon as he reached her that she was so happy to see him, and was looking forward to have a good and loving relationship. This is followed by embracing and kissing.

Densil	'You got a beautiful tan, Sadie, in such a short time. How are your folks?'
Sadie	'They are very well, and looking forward to seeing you. Crissie is always around. She too will be ever so pleased to see you.'
Densil	'Look who is here? 'Crissie'. You are looking so young and attractive. How nice to see you again. All my friends in England send their love for you.'

Crissie said to Densil. 'Sadie was always saying nice things about you, and she knew you would always be there for her.'

Densil embraced Sadie and gave her a loving kiss again.

Crissie was very happy for her friend.

Densil 'Where is the bathroom' he said to Sadie. 'I will have to have a quick wash, because I was so hot when coming from the airport.'

Sadie 'It is all there for you darling, Go on have your wash. I would even love to join you as well.'

'Densil' said Crissie, 'Guess who is here? Your friend Rodney and his wife.'

Rodney said to Densil, when he was having his bath, that he would love to take him to the seaside if all being well the following morning. 'Oh how exciting' said Densil? 'You know something? You are all so kind.'

Rodney 'It's our duty to welcome you to our island, you are such a nice and polite guy, and also very caring. Sadie said so many nice things about you.'

Densil 'It is a pity Sadie has to go modelling today, when that is all over we all will go to the seaside tomorrow.'

Sadie, Crissie, Rodney, his wife and Densil all prepared for their journey to the seaside. It was to be the highlight of his holiday. It was a day of feasting, a day of games, and a day of romancing, which prick a hole on their emotions when spending a day at the seaside. The atmosphere was so overwhelming that Densil and Sadie promised to return the following day.

Crissie said she could not make it because she had to go to the market the following day. It was all down to Rodney and his wife Maisie to make up their minds if they would be able to arrange another day at the beach.

Sadie 'What on earth am I going to tell my agents for not turning up for work two days on the trot?'

Densil 'Tell them you were not feeling well.'

Sadie	'How can I say that? Do you honestly think they will believe me? They suspect you are here and we are having a wonderful time.'
Densil laughed!	'What is better than having a wonderful time darling? Don't you think they are a bit jealous? You can make up for it by offering to work the following day, which would have been your day off.'
Sadie	'I am sure they will be pleased with this suggestion.'
Densil	I have a surprise for you, perhaps it's not a surprise really because you have been expectding this.'
Sadie	'What is it Densil?'
Densil	'Sadie, give me your finger, the third finger.'

Sadie was surprised although she was expecting it would happen before too long a time.

Densil	'Will you marry me.'
Sadie	'How exciting! Yes I will. You really are a darling.'
Densil	'I can't wait to have you as my darling wife. I can't wait to have you sharing my life.'
Sadie	'I am really thrilled. Mum and Dad will be pleased, so will Crissie and all our friends.'
Densil	'When are we going to plan for that big day? First we must get in touch with the vicar for an early date.

Densil and Sadie went to see her mum and dad concerning their big day. They all planned together, who to invite and what they should prepare for the feast. Everything was carefully planned for the special day. The dress, the presents, everything was wonderful. They were all happy and the bride and bridegroom went off for their honeymoon, and to start a new life together.

'Sadie' have you seen my razor darling' said Densil. 'I left it in the bathroom. Sadie you forgot to put away the toothbrush and paste as well.'

Densil	'My maid used to do that for me. Lucky you!'
Sadie	'What did your maid die of?'
Densil	'Embarrassment.'
Sadie	'Well if you think I am going to be your maid you can forget it. I will just go back to my parents.'
Densil	'I am ever so sorry to upset you darling.'
Sadie	'Here are your dirty socks and handkerchief, do not leave them on the floor.'

She threatened to go back to her parents if he does not stand up to his responsibilities.

Densil	'How can you do this to me dear, when we haven't even finished our honeymoon? Some of the guests may not have returned home as yet.'
Sadie	'I am upset with you for asking me for this and that. You are an adult, so behave like one.'
Densil	'If that is your attitude towards me, I might as well never have married you. It's amazing how quick you have changed from my darling girlfriend to my darling wife in such a short time.'
Sadie	'Things would be better if you could stand up to your responsibilities.'
Densil	'Please Sadie don't go. I promise you I will not push you around as my little maid.'
Sadie	'Oh Densil, I will forgive you, but please, please never do this again.

Densil	'Yes I will not do it again.'

Sadie said to him that she had seen a strange figure like a ghost lurking around the living room. 'I saw it two times. I believe it means to scare the life out of me. I know I am in danger of this awful figure. I know I am in danger for if nothing else had happened, my reason would certainly fail me, unless I escape this building soon.'

Densil	'Are you sure that what you saw was a ghost?'
Sadie	'Yes, it was really a ghost, and I am really scared, really scared. I hate to think of it nevertheless seeing it. It must have been four o'clock when I heard the sound in that smelly room at the far end of the living room. It sounded as if someone was dropping balls on the floor.'
Densil	'I can see the nervousness in your face, and to be honest I am worried over you. We will have to call the vicar to exorcise this house as soon as possible.'
Sadie	'Let us go to the nearest library to see if there is anything mentioned about the ghost in our home.'

When they went to the library, to their amazement it was a well known fact that the house was a haunted one.

Densil	'Sadie, we will have to leave this house as soon as we can. I hope your parents will be able to offer us a room or two in their house until we are able to have one of our own. We will call your mum and tell her the bad news about the haunted house, and our experience.'
Sadie	'Mum, good morning. How is Dad and the rest of the family keeping?'
Mum	'Fine. Dad is well and nevertheless longing to see you and Densil.'

She told her mum that she saw this ghost lurking around the house where they are living and she and Densil would love to come and share their house until they could buy one of their own.

Sadie's mum was very sorry when she heard of her experience and offered them a place in their home straight away.

Densil   'We can ring Crissie and tell her the good news. This is really good news.'

Sadie   'Really fantastic. Densil I am not feeling well, I would love to have a lie down.'

By this she was thinking that she was pregnant. She thought to herself that she should see her doctor, because she had missed her period.

Densil   'How are you Sadie, darling?'

Sadie   'Not too good. I am thinking of going for a check up.'

Densil   'A check up?'

With a broad smile on his face, he suspected that Sadie had become pregnant.

Sadie   'Don't be too excited, Densil. It may not be. However if it is we'll be laughing.'

Densil   'This could never have come at a better time when we are preparing to stay with your mum and dad. They too will be glad as we are. Imagine hearing the patter of tiny feet around the house.'

Sadie   'Good morning doctor. I am not feeling too well and I have not seen my period in six weeks, therefore I am wondering if I am expecting a baby.'

Doctor   'Take your clothes off, so I can give you a thorough examination. Yes, you are really expecting your first child.'

Sadie   'Oh! How wonderful. I am so thrilled. I can't wait to tell my darling husband that he will be a father and my mum and dad, they too will be grandparents.'

Sadie   'Guess what we are going to be parents soon.'

Densil   'How wonderful, I am so pleased, really pleased. Then when is our baby due? I can't wait to hold our baby.'

He said with a broad grin.

Sadie   'I would love to have a baby girl, we could call her Anabella. That's a beautiful name.'

Densil   'I am excited and indeed not bothered whether the baby is a he or she, providing the baby is normal.'

Sadie   'Of course I do not mind as well. Anyone will do, for we can always try again.'

Sadie   'Oh Mum, I am expecting a baby.'

Mum   'Oh! How refreshing, your father will be happy for you. I can't wait to tell the rest of the family this wonderful, refreshing news. What to be a grandmother. Yippee, yippee, oh we are going to have a grandchild.'

Mum   'Congratulations, my dear son. God bless you and Sadie. May his light shine on you in every step of the way.'

Sadie   'Thanks a million, Mum.'

Mum   'I have something to warn you about.'

Sadie   'I am waiting to hear about it.'

Mum   'Well since you are now living in this area, I must advise you not to wear your diamond ring and your expensive pearl necklace and earrings when you are going shopping or for a walk.'

Sadie   'Oh how caring and thoughtful a mother you are. I will surely avoid wearing them to certain

	places. I'm sure Densil will be pleased with you for warning me.'
Densil	'Where are you going today?'
Mum	'To the supermarket.'
Densil	'I hope Sadie will go along with you, she will be able to cope with the new area much better if she is in your company.'
Mum	Don't worry son.'
At the shop	
Sadie	'Look Mum, can you see that man dragging that screaming child down the embankment.'
Mum	'How evil can he be to drag that poor child, that screaming child. He must be a sick person. We have to ring the police and tell them what we saw. Come let us hurry.'
Sadie	'Let me have the police number so I can call them while you unpack the grocery. I am just ringing to tell you that I saw a scruffy man dragging a screaming child down the embankment at Portobella Railway.'
Policeman	'Thanks for telling us. We will be going to investigate this. It could be a serious offence.'
Sadie	'Mum, the police are going out right now to see what happens.'
Mum	'I am a bit nervous, suppose that scruffy geyser raped that poor girl or even murdered her.'
Sadie	'I am nervous too.'
Mum	'Densil will be very worried for us, I suspect the police are going to ask us to identify that man.'

Police (this was led by Inspector Henry)

Hello Sadie, will you be able to assist us in our enquiries, at first it was an abduction, but I am afraid now it is a rape and indecent assault.'

Sadie 'Oh my God, I am really frightened not because you need me to be a witness, but because of what has happened to that poor girl.'

Police 'I will come around to see you and your mum to put together some identity of the man.'

Police Henry 'We will hold an interview in a nearby house close to where the girl was snatched. It is difficult trying to get information from some shoppers, especially after such a terrible incident as this. We rely very much on our specialist officers. What time was it when you saw this girl's abduction?'

Sadie 'It was around eleven fifty six approximately. So this was not really a very long process, because it is now twelve forty eight.'

Police 'That awful man could not be very far away. By now he may be lurking around in the brambles, where he maybe listening to the voices of people passing by and trying to hear what they are saying about his brutal act. You bet he is lurking around some corner.'

Mum 'You see my darling daughter, how some people can behave in certain areas, that's why I told you not to wear expensive jewellery around here.'

The victim's parents heard of this ordeal and hurried down to the police station to enquire who has done this dreadful thing to their daughter.

Police 'We do not know where he got your daughter from but she was seen with this scruffy man dragging her and she was screaming down an embankment. This fourteen year old girl has been raped in the most awful manner. We need to find the person who did it quickly before he strikes again.'

Parent	If I ever set my eyes on that bastard I'll break his flipping neck. How could he do that to my only daughter? She is just like an angel.
Police	'You leave this to me. This is my department. I promise you, we will do all we can to bring this beast to justice. We will leave no stones unturned, to catch him.'
Parents	'Can we see our daughter?'
Police	'You will be allowed after a couple of hours, because she is under sedation and cannot be disturbed.'
Mother	'Oh God, why my little angel, why her, why her? I can't take this. That evil bastard, that child molester, I hope you catch him soon before he strikes again. No child is safe around here until he's caught.'
Sadie	'What are we now going to do, because we will now be exposed when we give information to the police about the yobbo? Suppose he lives nearby, if that should be the case we will have to change our address. I wish such an awful thing did never happen.'
Densil	'We just have to weather the storm and hope he will be a gentleman and give himself up, by doing that we would be free from identifying him.'
Sadie	'That would be a wonderful thing. It would be amazing. However let's hope for the best.'
Police	'Hello Sadie. I have found that evil man who raped the girl biding in a shed opposite the railway station. He did not have to do much

questioning because he admitted he did it, because all the evidence was there.'

Victim's parents were relieved knowing that the evil man had been caught.

Densil 'Now that they have found him, all this headache has started to disappears. I was worrying silently, because I did not want Sadie to see how much I was worrying. We can now put this dreadful mess aside and concentrate on the baby that is on the way.'

Mum 'Not very long to go. I am so anxious to see and hold my baby. The days and nights seem so much longer. The waiting is just so long.'

Densil 'Sadie, let's go and do some shopping for our baby before it's too late for you, because you are now so big as the months advance. Where shall we go to do our baby shopping?'

Sadie 'Oh yes, let's go to this particular shop, the clothes there are so smart.'

Densil 'This baby will be one of the luckiest babies around, to have us as parents, plus a grandmother as dear as your mum. Come quickly. Listen to the song on telly. 'Oh come to the hall in the wild west' How appropriate. That really suits the yanks. That reallysounds wild indeed.

Sadie 'They really can dance and clap their hands. That is really exciting.

By this time Sadie was also in the mood to have a jig. She could even feel the baby moving in her tummy as if he or she was dancing).

Sadie How amazing, so you're the only one who is not dancing at the moment?'

Densil	'You wait. I will do all the dancing after our baby arrives. But surely you could have a dance, seeing I am and the baby as well. How exciting, to feel the baby moving as if it is really dancing.'
Sadie	'I will have to go for an examination at the doctor tomorrow to make sure everything is fine.'
Densil	'That means I will have to take the day off to go with you.'

At the doctor's surgery

Doctor	'Good morning Sadie, how are you?'
Sadie	'Fine, the baby is fine, I presume for I can feel the awesome movement especially when there is music playing.'
Doctor	'Good. Well let's see what your little one has been up to. Please lie on the couch so that I can examine you.'

After the doctor examined Sadie

Doctor	'Well the baby and everything is fine. You still have a week to go.'
Sadie	'Can't wait for that. The days feel so long, endlessly long.'
Doctor	'I hope the next time I see you it will be an easy one. Densil will be glad to hear that all is going well indeed.'
Sadie	'The doctor told me that everything is well with me and that our baby is fine. She is pleased and expects an early delivery. My darling, the waiting will soon be over, and we'll be holding a precious baby.'
Densil	'You know something Sadie. I think this baby is going to be glorious, because you are so beautiful. Sorry I can't say that of myself.'

Sadie	'Oh no you are a handsome guy.

They then kissed and laughed with a passionate twinkle in their eyes.

The following day

Sadie	'I'm not feeling well, therefore I have to put all the things I require for the delivery together.'

By this time Sadie started to feel real contractions

Sadie	'Densil, please call the doctor.'
Densil	'Doctor, Sadie asked me to call you, because she is now having contractions every five minutes.'
Doctor	'I will see you in ten minutes time.'
Densil	'Sadie, darling the doctor will be here soon.'
Sadie	'This pain is very severe, the contractions are getting more and more painful as the time advances.'
Doctor	'When was the last contraction?'
Sadie	'Roughly three minutes ago.'
Doctor	'Your wife is doing well.

By the time the doctor uttered these words to Densil, the baby arrived.

Sadie	'A girl, oh my little Annabelle.'

Mum was very happy when she came to learn that she had become a grandmother. She rushed to the hospital.

Mum	'I guess Densil is very happy for the pleasure you've brought him.'

Sadie telephoning her friend Crissie

'I've had my baby and she is a girl. She weighs in at seven pounds.'

Crissie	'Oh how wonderful, did you have an early labour.'
Sadie	'Not bad.'
Crissie	'I will come around tomorrow to see you and the baby. I am really glad for you.'

Crissie came around the following day, but to Sadie's surprise Crissie was not the same outspoken person she used to be. She hardy said anything about Densil, as she used to. Most likely Sadie said to herself that maybe she saw Densil with someone, maybe a strange girl, and she did not want to tell her.

Crissie	'I've got something to tell you.'
Sadie	'What is it.'
Crissie	'It's very hard to tell you.'
Sadie	'Don't worry. Please tell me because that will make me sad if you go away without telling me.'
Crissie	'Well I don't know about telling you, because it is going to upset you.'
Sadie	'Please, please do tell me.'

Crissie, hugging up to Sadie told her that she saw Densil with another woman, and she is sure they are having an affair.

Sadie	'Oh no, not after all my experience in pregnancy and having made him a very proud father of this beautiful daughter. I am really sad. How will I tell mum and dad about this awful thing. They will be very mad with him. They have always treated him like a son, with all the respect one could ever think of.'

Sadie rings her mum

Sadie	'I have bad news for you about my two timing rat. Densil is having an affair. No wonder he was always dressed up and usually out too late.

Mum	'Was all of this a terrible surprise to you?'
Sadie	'Yes it was.'
Mum	'Do you have any idea why there's been all of this psychological problem, brought on your pregnancy, or was it just some wild stupid thing?'
Sadie	'I think most things you do in life, you do it because you want to. I think ultimately you want to do something and you do it.'
Mum	'How did you hear about it?'
Sadie	'My best friend told me about it, because she was so upset with his behaviour.'
Mum	'Before you even talk to him, let us try to put on a brave face. Is there an explanation? I mean can he say something where you would say yes I understand I can forgive you.'
Sadie	'I don't think it's a question of understanding.'
Mum	'Is it forgiving?'
Sadie	'Forgiveness is rather a difficult subject, something that has to be completely worked out. I can't possibly see me doing that.'
Mum	'Never again will I trust that two timing rat.'
Sadie	'Never, oh yeah.'

Densil came home that afternoon

Sadie	'I heard something about you and another woman. Are you having an affair with this woman?'
Densil	'I'm not having an affair. I saw this woman and we decided to go for a drink in the hotel nearby, but that was all to it. Who told you about this? I guess my friend from work must have told Crissie and then she told you.'

Sadie	'Never mind who told me. Is it true you two timing rat?'
Densil	'Well I might as well tell you the truth. I am really having an affair. It started out innocently, but then it ended up not being innocent. Please forgive me, please, please.'
Sadie	'How can I forgive you after all of what my family and I have done for you?'

Densil stormed out of the house without even looking at Annabelle

Mum	'You have been honest all of your days, I can't understand why he did what he did.'
Sadie	'He'll probably go for a while, because this is very embarrassing for him. God knows how he is going to overcome this situation.'
Mum	'What are we going to tell the rest of the family. We have been betrayed by this stupid selfish monster.'
Sadie	We got to tell the family about this unfaithful rat.
Mum	This is really the hardest thing for anyone to tell one's family.

Densil returns to say how sorry he is.

Densil	Hi Sadie, I am really sorry to have let my family down, but it is one of those situations where my weakness got the better of me. I am fed up of being a love cheat. I have never been loyal to a woman in my life. I had two families and I cheated on both mothers. Now I want to change my ways.
Sadie	What on earth are you saying? I do not understand. Please repeat properly. I think I am hearing a different voice. I did not for one moment think that you had two different baby

	mothers. How can you possibly do that to Annabella and I?
Densil	I must tell you the truth. I have four more children by two other women, but was not married to any of them. There are two boys and two girls from those relationships. Each one had a boy and girl. The boys are the elder of the pair.
Sadie	I am almost speechless, yes almost speechless. What a waste of my loyalty to you. The family thought the world of you now it will be all gone. How could you! How could you!
Densil	I was never a good partner or father and now I am really it? Right now I am feeling void. I have not seen those four children for five years and have not sent them birthday or Christmas cards. My conscience is bothering me now. I have to make up to you and Annabelle for the pain I've caused. I am sorry I can't explain why I did this to you. I was yearning to meet someone like you to be faithful to, then imagine my dream came through and I blew it by having a fling with another woman when you were having our baby. Please forgive me, I am feeling so worthless.
Sadie	You must have had a miserable childhood life, why you are so insecure? Were you abused? Well something must have gone absolutely wrong why you fail to have a loving and fulfilling relationship. I really cannot understand this situation. What will I tell Annabelle when she is old enough to understand, furthermore what will I tell my mum and the rest of the family. Not forgetting Crissie? You are passing the same pattern to your children, think what impression it gives them that you haven't bothered to visit them let alone

supporting them. You must make an effort to see them as often as you possibly can.

Densil   You are such a babe! I am feeling pain for the upsets I've caused you. If only I could turn back the clock. It is too late now, but I am making you this pledge that I will never have an eye for another woman.

Sadie   I will arrange for you to see a counsellor who will help you come to terms with your past so that you can see things in a different light.

Sadie went to see Mum.

Sadie   How are you.

Mum   Fine.

Sadie   I am well. I just thought of coming around to see you and nevertheless to let you know that I have asked Densil to see a counsellor.

Mum   What for? I could have told you that just when I heard he had an affair that something was odd about him. Probably he was drinking too much and there were other things on his mind why he had behaved like that. My feeling is that he suffered from some deep and unexplained psychological insecurity about himself or his family background.

Sadie   You are so right mum, you hit the nail right on the head. He said he is so sorry for the pain and discomfort he has caused us. I hope, I will be able to forgive him. You know mum he's got four children with two women. He has not supported them neither has he visited them.

Mum   Then dear how on earth will you manage with a husband like Densil? He has deceived us, we have treated him with respect, so why shouldn't he treat us likewise. That's always something to fear when one has a different background.

Sadie Any assertive behaviour on our part could just make things worse and cause him to go into deep despair. This is not the kind of relationship I was expecting from my husband. You know mum I find it very hard to hate him for what he has done.

Mum I know you have my darling. The Lord will bless you for your kindness towards that rat of yours. I only hope he will change for the better.

Densil came to see where Sadie was when he visits her mum

Densil Mum, I am indeed sorry for the pain I caused. I hope you find it possible in your heart to forgive me.

Mum Densil, it is so hard. Why have you let us down so badly? We have given you all the respect one could ever imagine. I can see you obviously had a strange background. My Sadie was so kind and compassionate to you then look what you've done? Not only did you lie in the beginning for having two other women with four children. Then to make matters worse you cheated on my daughter/granddaughter. How could you! You will have this on your conscience for the rest of your life.

Densil Do please forgive me. I don't know what came over me when I met this girl.

Mum You should have known better. We have trusted you, we did our best to make you happy.

Densil I promise you this dreadful thing will never happen again. I have grown older and nevertheless wiser.

Mum	Well Densil for Sadie's sake and your beautiful daughter. I hope things will change for the better.
Sadie	Hi Densil and mum. I am back from the market. The things were so expensive. I did not know what to buy. I am glad I went out so that you both could have a little chat without me interfering. I hope there will be more understanding between us all.
Densil	I have vowed to mum to change my ways and do the normal things.
Sadie	Mum I think he will be good, he made that vow with plenty of remorse.
Densil	Sadie, babe, what can we have to eat from the shopping you took?
Sadie	Not many things to choose from, for the goods were so expensive.
Densil	You should have told me you were going shopping, then I would have given you some extra money to meet your demands.
Sadie	You see Densil I just went in a hurry in order for you and mum to have a tete-a-tete.
Densil	You are so cunning Sadie, I don't know why I cheated on you, when you are the only person I really love. There is a lot for you to learn, when dealing with someone like me.
Sadie	I will prepare some dinner with the hope that you are going to help me in the kitchen.
Densil	No problem, just tell me where to get an apron. I will cut up the meat and have it seasoned while you prepare the vegetables.
Sadie	I am so sure mum and Annabelle will love this dinner because we have not had this kind for ages.

Densil	I am going for the wok in the cabinet. I love to cook my food in a wok. The food tastes so different. The flavour is so assuring. Our Anny will love this dinner seeing we are both preparing this together. We will notice her little mouth getting watery for this tasty dish of food.
Sadie	Densil, we should invite Crissie around for dinner when she is on her days off work. I am sure she will appreciate this a whole lot. She will notice you have changed and we are together as a happy and united family again.
Densil	Sadie, ring Crissie and ask her to come around for dinner.
Crissie	How wonderful of you to invite me around for dinner. I will endeavour to come. It's a pleasure I have been wondering and worrying about you all. Now I am overjoyed to have an invitation from you. How fantastic.
Sadie	I have never forgotten you my darling. I have always had you on my mind, but the time was not appropriate for us to invite you, seeing the ups and downs I was having with Densil. However he has promised to change. One thing I am looking at a changed person. I hope he will continue improving.
Crissie	This is wonderful news. I am really happy for you and Annabelle. A man who shows some determination is a man who has got belief in himself. You have the power within you to make your world your environment just what you want it to be. You have created mentally a life for yourself through your own intuition. You have always been so inpsirational.

Sadie	Look Crissie you have not decided on the date as yet? I know you are overwhelmed with joy to know we are together, after he stormed out of the house. This was not for long, but there was a lot of difficulties surrounding his past. That was the reason why we were so quiet. Things have changed after I tried together with the help of my mum. Without her presence I do not think I could have coped under the pressure.
Crissie	Sadie your mother is really a wonderful person. I know she would always be there for you and Anny. Sadie, I will be around on the 8th of June. Be on the look out for me. What must I bring for you and Densil?
Sadie	Oh Crissie, don't worry your dear self. We are just longing to see you and to have a lovely meal and a drink to renew our friendship. Good love never dies and the memories never fade away. This is one theory I am really sure of.
Sadie	Densil, I have asked Crissie and she said she would be coming over on the 8th of June to have dinner with us. She was really excited and nevertheless glad when I phoned her. She was really happy for us. You know Densil she is such a wonderful and caring person. She worries when things are not going right between us. That's why I have so much respect for her. She is a darling, a darling indeed. I have always examined her loyalty. One scarcely finds a loyal person nowadays. They are so wrapped up by their own selfishness. We cannot say this about our dear Crissie.
Densil	I am hoping she will enjoy our dinner, a lovely drink and our company. You bet she will be surprised to see the size of Anny and how

intelligent she is. This will be my chance, a wonderful chance to break the bad habits I had in the past by proving to Crissie that I can remedy the past.

Sadie Forget the mistakes you have been making in the past. Think of the opportunity that now presents itself to you. The habit of speaking positive words will help you to overcome the awful past. Time was is past time present is the time to make a fresh start and this is the time to weather the storm.

Densil You are so right my babe. I am so really thrilled to hear these positive words.

Sadie Look who is coming through the gate! Crissie, she is looking so elegant and happy.

Crissie Good evening Sadie and Densil. How wonderful to see you. I was looking for this wonderful reunion. I am so happy to be a guest to your home again. This is beautiful and I am proud.

Densil I know from the bottom of my heart that my life will be better third time around.

Crissie What do you mean by this third time round? I only thought you had Sadie alone before you had this affair with this other woman.

Embarrassment for Densil to explain himself.

Sadie You see Crissie he had two other women with four children before he met me. He kept silent about them until his conscience prick a whole on his emotions. I was absolutely flabbergasted, but since he told me without me finding out, I thought that was honest of him to come clean.

Crissie Life always has a little problem, but if one will remedy that problem then it will be nice to go forward in the right direction.

Sadie	I have forgiven him because he has vowed to change.

Densil in a melancholy voice

Let's have this dinner with the fullest assurance that my horrible life has changed for the better.

Crissie	Where is little Anny?

As soon as she uttered this little Anny entered the room. She kissed and hugged her gently.

Crissie	You are a sweet little girl. I was longing to see you just to have a cuddle and a kiss and to see your sweet smile.

Sadie	She was always asking for you, so I can imagine what she is thinking as she is not capable to show her emotions as yet.

Crissie	The entire family must be proud of her.

Densil	Let us eat this dinner we have prepared especially for you. I know we will all enjoy this dinner.

Sadie to Crissie and Densil

I'm sure we will.

Crissie	This dinner is breathtakingly nice! This dinner I will never forget.

Sadie to Densil and Crissie.

I am sorry I did not tell mum to come around for dinner as well. I'm sure she would enjoy this and furthermore she would be very pleased to see you.

Densil	All you have to do Sadie is to arrange another get together, then we can invite Rodney and his family plus a handful of close friends if it is OK by you?

Sadie	I was thinking of that myself, so it was nice of you to suggest this. I can see we are thinking positively on the same wavelength.
Densil	Crissie, I am so proud to have Sadie as my wife and best friend. She is so understanding and nevertheless full of wisdom.
Crissie	I always knew she was a wise woman, someone to have as one's best friend.
Sadie	I really enjoy these compliments, but I do not think I fit all what is said about me. Still it is nice to know someone has something good to say about me.

Densil to Crissie

My Sadie was always a positive woman with a lot of love in her heart. She lived her life happily. She will take care of everything that happens to her whether it is positive or negative. What a clever woman. she had given all that was good in herself regardless of her health to others. This love is without selection or exclusion.

Sadie to Densil

One should live in principle. If one's intentions are intense enough, loving actions will follow as sure as night follows day. True love will embrace all beings everywhere, whether it is human, creatures, animals and plants.

Densil

I really feel privileged to have you babe. You are better than a million diamonds in crusted ring. With all what I have done and you remain so faithful and kind.

Sadie to Densil

I am happy with those kind words and I am hoping I will continue to be an example for all. There can be true happiness after an affair. The thing that is usually bad after an affair, is if it is denied by the one who has it. They usually defend themselves by ill-treating the honest partner. This was not the case with you. You said it without conviction. The only thing I did not approve of is the children you had with those two other women. Then again if you had mentioned before we were married I would not want you. So you see you are clever indeed.

Densil with a broad smile

I had to do what I had to do. I loved you and there was no way I was going to let those things that passed be a hindrance. Now I have your love and your patience and nothing, nothing in this world will change this. I was a fool, an idiot to have an affair after you had Anny. My regrets and my apologies I will always repeat.

Sadie   Densil, I would love to go back to work to pursue my career as a model.

Densil   How appropriate. A model. I never thought when I met you in the beginning not only where you putting on fashionable clothes, you had this in your mental ability to be a model to all. This is more rated to me than just trying on clothes. Well what can I say? If you feel like doing that again I will not say no.

Sadie   I know Anny is going to miss me, but I am hoping she will adopt to her new career within a short time, she is such an easy going child. I doubt there will be any problems.

Densil   Well if that's what you desire, that desire must be fulfilled.

Sadie   Oh that's nice of you Densil not to object. However your objections would not have stopped

	me from doing my modelling. This is one of the few things in life I really want to do.
Densil	No problem. I can handle that OK. Well I have to spend more time with Anny seeing you will be away for up to two weeks sometimes.
Sadie	That's right. We are a family therefore we have to share the time between us for Anny's sake.
Densil	It will not be long before she starts going to nursery. Some nurseries take them when they are three years. I think three years is a bit too young for Anny.
Sadie	Densil, remember her carer to be will help us to read to her. She will also teach her to write and draw. She is a caring person. I'm sure you know the one I am talking about. She lives just around the corner from the primary school.
Densil	I was thinking of another one down the lane from the lake where Rodney used to fish. What is the name again?
Sadie	Montego Lane. That's the one.
Densil	Sadie sometimes I find it hard to remember the name of a road or lane. Maybe I am getting absentminded.
Sadie	Densil the best of persons forget sometimes.
Densil	Your mum and dad will be happy to hear that you will be going back to do modelling again. They will be seeing more of Anny when she starts going to her carer because their home is just nearby.
Sadie to Densil	I got a letter from the firm and she said I must b e present on the 22nd of June.

Densil	Oh! Your endeavour has come to pass and I am happy for you my babe.
Sadie	I definitely want to do it, and that is all down to me. I yearned for the opportunity for a long time, but could not get the courage of when to start. Your blessing will surely give me that determination I needed. I yearned for this opportunity for a long time, but could not get the courage of when to start. Your blessing will surely give me that determination I needed.
Densil	I'm sure you needed that co-operation. I will be behind you in every way I possibly can.

Sadie to her Employer

> Good day I am glad to be back.

Employer	I am indeed happy to have you back Sadie. You are looking very well indeed. You are looking much healthier in appearance. I am sure you will be bringing a lot of fresh air around us. You are certainly going to motivate us by your fresh appearance and your charm.
Sadie	How can you say that when I haven't even started?
Employer	Just by looking at you I can tell. I am sure the staff will be happy to see you again. Sadie, you already know what to do, therefore you can get on with it.
Sadie	Right.

During lunch break Sadie was approached by some of the staff selling drugs. This was the last thing on her mind. She was actually forced to take this deadly cocktail as this was the first time in her life someone had recommended drugs to her, she thought of giving it a try This she did and regretted it.

Sadie	Densil, my day was good in a way, but I must tell you that I have been introduced to drugs and I

have taken some for the first time. I was having this kind of flying effect and I do not know if it is contributed to the drugs.

Densil   Oh no! What have you done my babe? Please please for God's sake do not take it again.

Sadie   I promise you Densil I will never take it again.

Densil   Is there anything I can do for you just to stop those awful people introducing drugs to you?

Sadie   I can handle it Densil.

As soon as Sadie went to work, she was approached with drugs again and she took it because she became addicted to it. Densil became worried and visited Sadie's workplace and confronted her about her drugtaking.

Sadie   I know what you are saying and I understand, but look I am fine.

Densil   I know what you are going through that notion of going back to work after a long spell of having Anny and myself to cope with. But you must remember it was your sole desire.

Sadie   I know, I know. if I want to do it occasionally, it's up to me. I will not be doing it every day.

Densil   Has your employer noticed that you are taking drugs?

Sadie   I don't think he has noticed. I tried to be as discreet as possible.

Densil   You have to see the doctor urgently. I am really concerned over you. I will ring for an appointment for you. You will get a letter from the doctor in a short time to attend a clinic for treatment. This habit has to stop. Your becoming a drug addict and I am afraid of that. Don't forget you are a parent and furthermore you are my wife. I feel like I am going to crack up. The pressure of seeing you taking drugs is too much to bear. Sadie, what on earth has led you to take drugs? I know you have been through a lot over the years, but it is now history. You have forgiven me and that was great. You were very supportive in every single way. I am sick to the teeth. I can't understand why drugs. If you had told me your feelings, I would have done something about it.

Sadie   You could not have known Densil because it was forced on to me at work and I tried it. I am just as mystified as you are at this moment in time. If only I could turn the clock back. It is just too late to say I am sorry. I have broken your poor heart already, just as you have broken mine before.

Densil   Let bygones be bygones, and let's turn another page.

FAITH

Faith is not only worshipping
In the Cathedral on a rainy day.
Faith is not only giving
To the poor and needy in our land.
Faith is not only loving
Everyone in the village or in the town.
Faith is not only waiting
For wonderful things to happen.
Faith is the wonderful endeavour,
The enormous celebration,
With the attitude to serve
Whatever that comes along
No matter how good or bad,
To whom or where it happens.
Faith is the language to learn
That people from distant land,
Are just alike as thee in body and soul.
Faith is to love the days it rains,
The days when the sun shines
And the days when there is neither
Rain nor shine.
We have a faithful Father,
That goes in and out with us,
And what can be the use of 'Him'
Is more awesome than I can tell.
Faith is the attitude to love the Divine
So you better have faith! Faith! Faith!

ENGLAND LAND OF FREEDOM

E ngland the country where the rich, the famous
   And the under priviledge lives
N for nobility and noble in this ideal island
G for the Government many other countries are craving for
L for the language everyone should endeavour to learn
A for aristocrats, the artists and animal rights people to
   Stamp their authority
N for the nonsense neither of the National will tolerate
D for democratic, development, despite the forces of endeavours.

L and of freedom for all its residents
A for the altar in our Cathedral
N for National Security everyone craves for in time of need
D for disease where there is always a diagnosis.

O for office we all love to enter
F for fulfilment in our Father's land

F for friendship in a friendly atmosphere
R for racehorses the best in the world for its breeding
E for Evangelist, Elizabeth our Queen and English language
E for everlasting peace and love
D for dominance to get things we believe in
O for order of the garter
M for Majesty for which there have been many.

MONGRELS

Mongrels that's what we are?
God created two people for one world
They co-habitated in the Garden of Eden
And Cain and Abel came along
How dare you say we are not one
And one for all.

Mongrels that's what we are?
Some went to faraway lands
To hide the grey area that nature brings
Mongrels start changing like a rainbow in the sky
Some change by the shining sun
While some change by the winter breeze

Mongrels that's what we are?
The water we drank, the air we breathe
The food we eat, the sun we tanned in
Are the reason for our changes
From the land in the garden of Eden

Mongrels that's what we are?
Dark eyes, slittery eyes, blue eyes, brown eyes
Curly hair, straight hair, short hair, long hair
Black, brown, white and pink
How did all these colours come along?
Just like the rainbow in the sky

Mongrels, mongrels that's what we are?
Kings, queens, black and white
Peasants, noble, humble and wise
We are all mongrels, for we are not what we were at first
God made us in his own image
Now we have all sorts in this land
Mongrels, mongrels, mongrels forever mongrels.

Some said we have third and first world
Now where is the second I'll like to know
Some brought wars and scars to this land
Some brought tears and fears in our hearts
Mongrels, mongrels that's what we are?

May peace and love be the epitome of our dreams
And accept that we are mongrels hence
We should live in peace and harmony.

LEARN AND EARN

Learn and earn – er – ern
Reap and sow – o – o;
That's the way to earn and learn – er – ern

Mow and sow – o – o,
Reap and sell – e – el;
That's the way to earn and learn – er – ern.

I have learnt many things – e – ings
When selling my strings – e - ings,
That's the way to earn and learn- er – ern.

Learn and earn – er – ern,
Reap and sow – o – o;
That's the way to learn and earn – er – ern.

You've seen it before – or – ore
And that's the way to learn and earn – er – ern.

JUST ONE BREATH

Just one breath to be grateful
For what you have achieved;
Just allow divine love to enter in
Breathe deeply for a minute
Just one breath.

Just one breath, be honest,
Say what you mean
Just one breath
Don't simply turn fear into depression
By screaming and yelling
Just one breath!

Just one breath if someone upset you
Very often when we lose our temper
Before we answer just take one breath
Just one breath!

Just one breath before you take that trip
Just one breath, just one breath
Change the language you use
And alter the whole emphasis
Just one breath, just breathe deeply
Just one breath.

O WORLD

O world so free, we love 'Thee'.
O world so fearful, we love 'Thee'.
O world so beautiful, we love 'Thee'.
O world so delightful, we love 'Thee'.
O world so wonderful, we love Thee.

O world so green, we love Thee
O world so blue, we love Thee.
O world so dry, we love Thee
O world so wet, we love Thee.

O world so endless, we love 'Thee'.
O world so forgiving we love 'Thee'.

O world, O world, I saw you in my dream
You who effervesce – my hope, my friendship
And endeavour,
O world! O world ! O world! I love Thee.

A LIAR

You know where you are with a thief,
You know where you are with a rapist.
You know where you are with a murderer,
But you never know where you are with a liar.

A liar is always someone to fear,
A liar is capable of doing everything
To turn one's life upside down,
'So' turn not your back on a liar.

There is always a smirk on a lying face,
Evil is the world to describe a lying tongue
And I also think it is an abomination to the Lord.

A liar is someone who wears people down,
They even have two faces
And you'll never know if you're down or up.

All tyrants seem to be perfect liars
Who manipulate people at their peril
Then laugh at their success.

SINCE WINE IS THE DRINK

Since wine is the drink for my wedding serve on?
Fill my glass, let it run over and over
Let me drink of it, for it is love.

Table, tables many tables I have
Bring the buckets the big cold ones
Now serve the wine from the coldest bottles
Wine and dine me in the hall
Then wine and love me till the hours are small.

I'll drink on! Many bottles I drank
Let me be merry, till the boys are up for pranks
Then give me more and more I say.

Since wine is the drink for my celebration,
Drink on!
Share my wine and drink to my happiness
For I am in bliss and this cannot be a missed.

ABUSE

I walk the road with houses along,
To hear people playing amusing songs;
It never was! It was dangerous and revolting.
It was full of urban savages, drug abuse
Fuelled with anger from alcohol and resentment.

Help us Father as I kneel and pray,
We are seeing aggression in our streets.
Help us to overcome this dangerous attitude.
We are Your little children and we are crying
Help them to regain their sanity, oh Gracious Lord.

Why! Oh why! Have the changing faces so anxious.
Why are they allowed to have access to alcohol
Twenty and four hours of the day
Seven days a week, four weeks a month
Help the perpetrator oh Merciful Lord.

We need You to guide us, oh Merciful Father
We are seeing things we cannot visualize
The earthquake, hurricane, drought,
And now tsunami has taken its toll
Oh help us Your Great Majesty
We are Your children and we are in pain.

Our children are now becoming forest savages
Their behaviour has become serious violence
Resulting maybe in death, or wounding
This is serious and we need Your helping hand
Help them please! I am crying to You Lord
We are Your little children and there is no gain.

THE SQUIRREL AND THE CAT

There lived on the farm of my uncle Bob a squirrel and a cat. These two can never be friends. They are at loggerheads with each other. The cat is always chasing the squirrel up the tree and on the fence.

One day the cat, who's name is Tabby, vowed to catch the squirrel. The squirrel heard this threat and decided to tease this poor cat. The squirrel would climb the fence in a slothful manner for the cat to feel very sure that she would catch the squirrel. Up and down the squirrel ran. 'Ha! Ha! Ha! You can't catch me' said the squirrel. The poor cat was left frustrated and very tired. 'You stupid squirrel' said the cat, 'why can't you stop making a fool of yourself? Why don't you have a run on the lawn or in the meadow?' 'No' said the squirrel, 'I am not very agile on the flat surface.'

Up the wall, up the tree and on the fence that's where my true skill lies.' 'You silly bushy tail squirrel, I cannot understand you at all,' said the cat. 'One day soon I will teach you not to steal my uncle's nuts and his apples from his farm. You must learn to work for your living' said the cat. 'What?' said the squirrel. 'Please take that word back. You see those mighty oak trees I am the one who sew the acorns which grew up to be a mighty tree.' 'Ah!' said the cat, 'That was not intended, you was just a greedy creature who could not bear to leave the acorns on the ground. You are a thief' said the cat. 'No,' said the squirrel. 'I only want to see a big tree in Bob's garden. By that way I can have you frustrated more and more. I am sure Bob loves me' said the squirrel. 'Bob loves me more than you' said the cat. 'No! No! No! No! No!' said the squirrel.

LITTLE BLUE BIRD SONG

Raise it, raise it to the roof, the little blue bird sang. How can you sing so melodiously? The song bird chirped. I'll raise it, I'll raise it as loud as I can said the little blue bird. You just talk to me while I sing my song. You cannot be serious said the little blue bird! Ah! Said the song bird I can sing like the nightingale in the highest bush when I am singing a song with highest praises. Only those birds that know my words, only they can sing my song, then teach the others to sing along.

One day soon my words will reach their ears which will help them through their ensuing years. Raise it, raise it my little blue bird, raise it high with lyrics so true. Oh! How I love my dear song bird, for she's so sincere a bird to me.

I'll raise my tune by the dawn of day, just before the donkeys are up for bray and continue till twilight draws near. I'll hum to you, then sing to her for she's my friend when we're having fun in the cherry tree. Cherries are good and are great for tea when having sop in the evening rain. I'll raise it loud and raise it clear for I'm the blue bird that sings my song. I'll raise it high from the top of the tree for all to hear me when I sing my song. Twita, twita, twee I hop and sing for all to hear me singing my song. Sing on! Sing on! the song bird said. Raise it, raise it we are here to listen to your melodious song. Twita, twita, twee, twee, I hop and sing, I'll raise it high on the top of a tree, so be prepared to 'bop' and hop.

TOM'S EXTRAORDINARY JOURNEY
TO THE STATES

Horace	Listen Matty, listen good, I heard Tom will be going to America to live and he will be taking with him all his belongings.
Hilda	Horace well my dear he is so greedy, I wondered how his family tolerated him for so long.
Horace	Well to be honest I am glad that geezer is leaving.
Hilda	This place will be a better one without him.
Horace	He was really a nuisance to many people. Everywhere he goes people complain about him.
Hilda	I hope when he goes to America he will have a little respect for the Yanks.
Horace	My dear Hilda, they will not argue, they will shoot first then ask questions after.
Hilda	What a thing that character will be up against.
Horace	I tell you my dear. This is a tough game.
Hilda	You mean over there.
Horace	Have you not listened on the telly about the shooting among schoolchildren over there?
Hilda	Sometimes I am so confused when I hear these things on the television or the radio. I just cannot believe that children as well as adults can do such awful things.
Horace	I do not think those children of crime have ever said the Lord's prayer.
Hilda	You got it so right!
Matty	Hilda girl, did you know that Tom was listening to every word we were saying?

Horace	I suspected that geezer would want to know if we were chatting behind his back.
Hilda	He must have hidden a tape, maybe behind the cupboard where we would not suspect the least thing.
Horace	How correct you are!
Matty	That's where he got all those ideas from.
Hilda To Tom.	I was telling Horace and Matty that you are from a very nice family.
Tom	Thanks very much, I hope you all will not be upset when I play this tape for you.
Hilda To Matty and Tom	
	You are free to play the tape for us.
Tom	Don't worry! Nothing serious, he muttered. I will plug this radio with the tape in into the socket on the wall, then you can listen to the contents.
Hilda	Matty I have forgotten my dinner on the fire, therefore I have to check on it quickly.
	They were so confused that Horace started to stutter.
Tom	Look! I will not be in the least upset about what is on the tape.
Matty	I will see you in the morning.
Tom	Well for a quiet life, I will not play the tape since there are so many confusions.
Horace	Then tomorrow you will be off to America?
Tom	Yes, tomorrow.
Hilda	I hope you will have a good life over there with the Yanks.
Tom	It is not hard for me to make friends. That comes naturally. Some people find it hard, but for me it is not a problem. Although I was really hurt, I did

not want them to know how much pain I was feeling.

Matty to Tom   May I wish you the best of luck in your endeavours.

Tom   Many thanks Matty dear.

Hilda   So you are really leaving us! Here is a small present for you from Horace and myself.

Tom   I am really chuffed by your generosity. It is so kind of you to remember me. After all, I said to myself, I was not the bad geezer they made me out to be. I can really hold my chin up. With a wide grin on his face he said thanks to them again.

Tom to Hilda and Matty
That was nice of you to be able to give such an expensive gift.

Tom's reaction towards the gift
Oh well! Oh well! What can I say, he quipped. All's well that ends well.

***

Hilda   Good day Tom.

Tom   A happy day to you my dear Hilda.

Hilda to Tom   Have you seen Matty and Horace?

Tom   No dear

Hilda   They will be coming around to say farewell to you.

Tom   I hope they will not be long, because I have to leave about eleven forty five to catch my coach which will take me to the airport, before one fifteen in the afternoon.

Hilda to Tom   I can assure you they will not be long.

Tom	Hilda, please open the door. There is a knock.
Hilda	It could be Matty and Horace, she uttered. Here comes Matty and Horace.
Horace	Good morning Tom, I am sorry we are a bit late. With a big hug and a kiss, he embraced Tom.
Matty	We are here to wish you a safe flight to America and that things will work right for all your endeavours.
Tom	Many thanks, many thanks, it is very nice of you all to be so kind and supportive to me.

Tom wished them a good future and promised to get in touch.

Hilda To Matty and Horace

Then Tom is really gone to the States. Good luck to him.

Tom on his way to the airport he thought within himself how awful it is to judge people's behaviour. After all he said to himself, they are not really a bad set of people, or is it my patience to pretend that nothing damaging was said. After all I am a very happy man now.

Tom was now on his way to America.

He thought within himself how happy he was and how he is going to get into acting business when he reaches the States.

Tom to the hostess

Hi, my name is Tom.

Hostess	My name is Anis
Anis	Tom, I heard England is now becoming like America. The fact that so many people are now taking drugs. The smoking of cannabis is now getting into fashion in your country isn't it?

Tom	It's crazy. Some people go out of their minds when they smoke. Honestly I think it is not a bad idea if some people with certain ills are allowed to use it in small quantities to relieve their pain.
Anis	What are you planning for the future?
Tom	To do a little acting if possible. I would like to go to the theatre to learn the art of how to be an actor.
Anis	That's a good idea. I wish you luck.
Tom	Thank you very much.
Anis	Well it is time for me to say bye! Bye! To you.

***

Tom went to ring Horace and Matty.

Horace	Phone's ringing
Matty	Answer the phone will you.
Horace	I will.
Tom	Hi Horace, this is Tom speaking.
Horace	I knew, I recognise your voice, I know for the distance sounds far indeed.
Tom	How are you all over there?
Horace	We are all well and nevertheless hoping for a pleasant weekend.
Tom	I have an invitation to go to the theatre for an interview regarding my acting career.
Horace	That was very quick.
Tom	Someone just gave me an invitation as soon as I came off the plane.
Horace	Oh now nice, I wish you the best in your endeavours.

Tom	I know it will be very tough, but that's all I wanted to do.
Horace	The weather over here is very bad. Every day it rains. The sun hardly ever shines.
Tom	Cheer up. You will soon start having good weather again. It may be late but it is still better than many other countries over the world, which may be suffering from an earthquake or hurricane.
Horace	You are so right. You know we are always moaning about something, when it is not one thing, it's another. Eh! So true.
Tom	Have you seen Anis recently? I spoke to her only for a short time recently, and she seems very bubbly.
Horace	Which Anis are you referring to?
Tom	The one that works as a hostess. I have only seen her two times, and thought she was very charming. We had a little chat on my flight here and would like to see her again.
Horace	I will ask my friend down the road to enquire when she is home for holidays.
Tom	That would be very nice of you, sometimes I feel very lonely and therefore have the desire for a friendly chat.
Horace	Who wouldn't.

Hilda came in the hall where Horace was

Horace	I am now speaking to Tom in the States.
Hilda	How is he?
Horace	Fine. He is better than us at this moment for at least his weather is good.

Tom	Is that Hilda's voice I am listening to in the background? Allow me to say hi to her. I will not be long.
Hilda	Tom is that you?
Tom	Yes it is.
Hilda	How are you my darling?
Tom	I am longing to see you folks already.
Hilda	There are so many people asking for you and wanting to know what you are doing.
Tom	Please tell them I am well and I am awaiting a result from an interview I had two days ago, apart from that there is not much on my plate as yet.
Hilda	I hope all will be well for you.
Tom	Thanks my darling. I went to get some shopping done this morning but the weather was not at all good. The rain was pouring down by the bucketful. I had to run for shelter under the canopy of a shop, a fast food one. You should be here to behold the size of the takeaways. A takeaway for a child could feed two grown men over there. I am not kidding it is the bare fact.
Hilda	No wonder most people over there have weight problems. It is a shame we over here are fast becoming just as bad. We certainly have to do something about the amount of food we are consuming.

Horace came into the room.

Horace	I can see you are still on the phone to Tom. He is such a character to speak to. One never gets weary of speaking to him. There is no idle talk with him, it's always pure fact.

Hilda	Here's the phone. You can wish him good luck in all his endeavours, and that we are looking forward to see him in the near future.
Tom	I'll see you soon, so take good care of yourself.
Horace	The same to you Tom.

***

Tom became anxious about the acting career.

Tom to himself	Speak aloud, well I must hurry on to the theatre where I had my interview to see if I am successful. Good day Mr Goodwin.
Goodwin	How are you?
Tom	I am fine. I am the person who applied for an acting job.
Goodwin	Oh yes I remember you.
Tom	Have I been successful?
Goodwin	Yes, but there is a small problem.
Tom	What is the problem? Is it something I can correct?
Goodwin	I'm sure you can if you try. Are you a citizen in this country?
Tom	No! I have a visa which will run for ten years.
Goodwin	That will do me fine. You said ten years, well that is more than the required amount I am demanding.
Tom	I am so very pleased to know the problem was not a big one. All is well otherwise?
Goodwin	Yes!
Tom	When can I start Sir?
Goodwin	At your earliest convenience.

Tom	I would like to start in three days time. This will give me a few days to put a few things together. I am so chuffed with my endeavours. I can assure you I am really going to work hard at this venture.
Goodwin	I am happy for your gladness, not many people are as fortunate as you, and I am glad you realise that.
Tom	I surely do. All my friends back home will be so excited to know I have been given a chance. Oh yes! Oh yes! My life will not be the same again. What a rejuvenation.
Goodwin	Please don't make too much fuss about it. We do not know of your ability to act. Actually so many people are just naturals. They just read a script and Bob's their uncle.
Tom	I hope I will be one of that kind. I am always good in giving gags. I just can't wait to get on with it.
Goodwin	Tom you can have your first go.

Audience listening to Tom's first crack. He had them all in stitches. He is electrifying to the crowd. Cool, some uttered, fantastic, some echoed. We are listening to this magnet of a man.

Goodwin.	It is hard to believe that someone can be so good, and he is only an amateur he said. When he is professional, what will he be like. I can't wait to see this character on stage. Now I can really say we've got the man.
Tom	I told you I wanted to do something, just to bring laughter to people's faces.
Audience	Tom, you have us all in stitches. We cannot tell the last time someone has ever achieved in making us laugh as much. Well done! Well done!

Tom	This is so flattering. I am chuffed with our kind words. You will get a lot more from me. This is really what I wanted to do for so long. I am a hungry man, so I will endeavour to do my best.
Audience	It is so nice to have someone like you. You are just a natural and good luck to you. We needed someone like you on the stage for a long while. Most of the greats have died or are really too old to carry on. Now we have you and that is good.

Tom rang Horace to give him the good news.

Hilda	Horace the phone is ringing.

Horace picked up the phone.

Tom	Hi Horace, this is Tom. I am thrilled to hear your voice. I was thinking about you last night. Don't you worry, it was something good. You'll never guess. I've got the job or career I always wanted to do. I always dream of this acting from when I was about seven years old. I have started and all the people who saw me are chuffed when they heard me performing. They were really a happy lot. They certainly enjoyed the evenings I had with them.
Horace	Tom, I know you are a clever guy when it comes to delivering a gag. You always show the tendency, to make people laugh. I am really pleased to hear that you got what you really wanted to do. Never mind going to a huge country like America. Tom, I know you will have a huge purse coming when things get around. I shall tell your friends over here of your achievement. Just be on your guard and you will be fine.
Tom	Life is really exciting over here, but one thing, one has got to be extra careful of gun men.

Young boys and even girls walk around with guns. It is so common over here, apart from that it is a wonderful country. Horace, I can assure you I will be taking precaution. I will make sure I do not visit certain places late at night. There are certain places where it is strictly a no go, after knowing this, I do not venture out.

Horace Well Tom, all my friends are in glee over your new career and are hoping to visit you soon.

Tom I am indeed sorry I have to stop talking to you now, because I have to get ready for the stage in a few hours time. Time really flies when one is speaking to a dear friend.

Goodwin Hi Tom, I am looking forward of seeing you tomorrow.

Tom You surely will.

Goodwin Good day Tom! I can see you are early. You are really the man we needed for a long time. Not only are you a great show person you are also loveable and punctual. We can do well with a lot of this.

Tom How flattering you are my dear man. When I behold goodness I'll endeavour to do my utmost best. That's why I am doing my best.

Goodwin We'll have a drink to that. What kind of drink can I pour you my dear man?

Tom Any old thing will do. Tell me what's on offer then I'll make my choice. Give me some of that old whisky. It can really juvenate the system. Sometimes one's body really needs a pick me up to get one going.

Goodwin I can see you surely like your drink.

Tom I surely do.

Goodwin	I myself like my stuff. It can really give me a great start.
Audience	Mr Goodwin, who will be filling us with laughter tonight? Is it that guy from England? He is so charming and so funny, he brought the roof down. It is amazing how some people are natural.
Goodwin	Only a few can be like that, and he is one of the few. Right now he is getting his costume ready for the act.
Tom	Hi there. This is Tom and I'm sure you remember me.
Audience	How can we forget you? You are our hero. You have reached the parts others have not reached for a long while.
Tom	Are you kidding?
Audience	No we are not.
Tom	You are a lovely bunch of bananas.
Audience	I hope you got no green ones today.
Tom	Only ripe ones, the sweet and firm ones.

Audience started to sing Harry Belafonte's song.

Tom	I was so chuffed with the audience.
Goodwin	Only this man can get you all in this mood. Thank heavens for this great man, at times like this we need a great person like you.
Tom	It is so good when one can bring out the best out of a person and I am here to do just that.
Goodwin	Tom, do you know you are a gift to me? You have saved me from the savagery of a recession. I was wondering for sometime that my business would have failed if I did not get a real person to

draw in the crowd for me. Now I have you and that is absolutely fantastic, really fantastic.

Tom   I am happy for your gladness. What more can I say? It is good to be good.

Goodwin   Please take a deep breath, listen to my name will you. Good-Win, fantastic isn't it?

Tom   You know something, I thought of it sometimes.

Goodwin   You didn't surely?

Tom   Yes I did. My show is meant to demonstrate what average people can do if they develop their ordinary powers.

Goodwin   I believe that education and entertainment are the same thing, your manner is deliberately informed to make people feel safe and confident in you. Sometimes they are inclined to have a go themselves.

Tom   That's my outlook young man! How precise you are! When I tell you some jokes sometimes, many of the people can definitely identify something during their lives that applies to what I am saying. They may even ask me to repeat again what I said. Man this makes them roar with laughter.

Goodwin   You've only got to try and you'll find the capacity of your mind will amaze you and your audience.

Tom   Perhaps because of my heightened state of mind, the air around me seems to fizz with electricity and magnetism, the strange coincidences keep occurring.

Audience   Tom have you ever been to Texas before? We are of the opinion that we have had someone fitting your image before. Sure electrical.

Tom	Coincidence is just one of the areas of the mind that seldom explores, but man when it comes, it can be magnetic.
Goodwin	I realised Tom had a real potential as an entertainer that's why I commissioned him to use his talents for us.
Audience	Tom we could spend all day with you and we'll never ever be bored.
Tom	That's what I am here to do and I enjoy every minute of it. I have to make an honest living therefore I have to do my best.
Goodwin	Yea man! The people are going bananas. They are loving every minute of your charm and your talent.
Tom	Sometimes I raise it and they raise it with me, you know sometimes that little sing song makes them tick.
Goodwin	Nothing is better than a man who can mesmerise the people as much as you can.

THE HONEST THIEF

A very long time ago there lived in a remote part of Neverland, a family of four and a few surrounding neighbours. A gentleman by the name of Dento wanted to make sure that his family had all that they could ever wish for. He told Maisie, his wife, that he was going to make a big garden in the forest, because the soil in the forest was so rich it would produce good crops. Maisie said how brilliant it was for him to suggest this. 'You are really a caring husband,' she said. Dento said he would be asking two of his neighbours to help him prepare the land for cultivation. This he did and the two men consented. They all set off for the forest to cut down the trees and destroy the grass and shrubs for the garden. When they went to the forest and started this hard task, there appeared some chimpanzees. 'Good morning' said one of the chimps to Dento. 'How nice of you to consider such a task,' said another. 'Yes,' replied Dento. 'I am making sure that my family will have all delicious food they need,' he went on. The chimp smiled at the idea because he knew what trick he would be up to when Dento planted his fruits and vegetables.

As Dento and his two workers prepared the ground, the chimp went and told the other chimps in the forest, that there was a nice man who has decided to cultivate a part of the forest, and that they should not get too near to frighten them. The three men planted bananas, plums, mangoes, yam, sweet potatoes, cabbage and tomatoes. They would go to the garden nearly every day to work on this wonderful vegetation. Dento's family hardly ever saw him during this period. 'Look,' said Dento to one of his workers, 'When these foods are ready we will sell them to the market traders.' Some of the crops took only four months to be harvested. He went to the local shops and asked them if they would buy some of his produce, because it was too much for his family to eat. The market traders told him that they would be very happy to sell his crop. As soon as Dento started to harvest the crops, the chimps joined in to steal the vegetables from the garden. The vegetation was so much that Dento did not realise that the chimp was stealing his vegetables.

This went on and on until the vegetables plot came to an end. This left Dento with the delicious fruits like the bananas, plums and mangoes. As soon as the fruits started to ripen, Dento and his two co-workers noticed that the ripe fruits were disappearing. They thought within themselves that some of their neighbours were stealing the fruit from the trees, especially the bananas. Dento suggested that he was going to ask someone to watch over his garden. The two workmen suggested he should ask the chimp that told them ho-de-do when he saw them working in the forest to act as a watchman. Little did Dento and the men know, that it was the chimp who was the thief. However, Dento asked the chimp if he could do this job for him. The chimp was so delighted as this was said to him. 'How wonderful you are Dento,' the chimp said. 'I have always yearned for a job like this to catch that thief. You have never done a better thing,' he muttered, 'I just want to catch that thief.' 'The pleasure is yours,' said Dento. 'Ha! Ha! Ha!' said the chirping chimp. 'I will be the best watchman in the forest.'

Dento went home and told Maisie and his three children his idea to allow a chimp to be the watchman. She said it was a bright idea. 'Look' said one of Dento's children. 'I would suggest unknowing to the chimp that you put some strong glue on the tree, that whoever climbs it, would stick to the tree.' 'How brilliant' said Dento and Maisie to their son. 'We always thought you were a very clever boy, but now you have proven it beyond words.' They said they would not tell the chimp their plan, just in case he was the one who was the thief.

They noticed after three days of asking the chimp to be the watchman, all the fruit that was ripe on the tree were still there, especially the bananas. The chimp was getting very hungry and decided to have a go at Dento's fruits again. He climbed the tree with a big bag and filled it with delicious fruits then he ate his stomach full. As he was ready to climb down he realised that he was stuck to the tree. He was there for about eight hours stuck to the tree, before Dento came to the garden. As Dento entered the forest he could see from a distance that the chimp was stuck to the banana tree.

He must have been the one who was stealing the fruits. He did not hesitate but ran to tell Maisie and the two workers what has happened. They said to him how brilliant his son was to suggest this trick. 'Now I have caught this thief, come with me' said Dento to Maisie and the two workmen. 'We will go to the forest and see the rascal about this monkey business.' When the chimp saw Dento he shouted, 'Dento please help me, help me I beg. I promise I will never do this again. I am begging you please, please sir help me. I beg you sir.' Dento said, 'You are the one that was stealing my vegetables and my fruits, I do not think I will set you free.'

The chimp started to call him Uncle Dento. 'Uncle Dento, Uncle Dento, Uncle Dento, I beg you please release me. I'll never, never do this again,' he muttered. 'I will never do this monkey business again.' Dento looked at Maisie and said, 'Shall I release him from the banana tree?' 'Yes,' said Maisie, 'under one condition that he works for you for two years without pay.' The chimp said, 'the choice is yours, providing you release me.' Dento released him and warned him never to do this again and you must not forget the promise you made,' said Dento. 'Yes' said the chimp.

As the chimp was released he ran home, as fast as he could, and did not return to that part of the forest. 'All this,' he said, 'is pure monkey business.' Dento was very sad because the chimp did not return to that part of the forest. He vowed never to make another garden in the forest again.

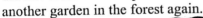

Millennium

As the dawn breaks and the sun rises
The earth and its inhabitants will soon be at play
Braying asses and mooing cows will soon be grazing
And trying to seek the warmth from the golden sun.

A new millennium has begun with dancing on the street
Millennium has come and changes have begun
This new millennium beckons a new era for reform
As the day begins to fade away twilight has begun
As the clamour and smoke of this festivity
Starts smouldering the battle has begun to manifest
A healthier age for one to compromise.

People of the world should get together
To change the evil and the poverty of this beautiful world.
We pollute the atmosphere as we fight for breath
We poison some plants, some rivers, some lakes.

Leaders must examine the problems of this world
Then solve them if they can
Families should get together with the knowledge
That they are one people
Then put the bad things right
We should spread a little happiness for this millennium
Then say farewell to those lonely days.

For this new millennium leaders of this world
Should show the nation that they are in control
Hence an example should be set
For some of our troubled folks
Then say farewell to those awful days.